My Pathway Through Cancer

'How to follow a different route'

Hazel Scade

Published by Hilltop Books

The contents of this book, based on the author's experience and research, are for educational purposes and the author does not advocate the use of any particular treatment. The aim is to acquaint the reader with alternative methods of treating cancer and for long-term prevention. Alternative treatments should be discussed with the patient's physician/doctor and ultimately the reader/patient must take full responsibility for their treatment.

Because risks are involved, the author expressly disclaims any responsibility for adverse effects of treatment that may occur.

Published by Hilltop Books

PO Box 7025, Bocking, Braintree, Essex CM7 9RZ

Printed by M&B Print Solutions Limited

ISBN 0-9542762-0-5

Acknowledgements

This book is dedicated to Christine, who spurred me on to being checked, without realising it. My heart goes out to Keith and the rest of her family whom she has left behind.

Thanks goes out to all my family and friends who gave much help and support through my difficult times.

Special thanks must go to Michael for understanding my feelings of wanting to seek a different treatment path. It was so much easier having him join me with the research, agreeing to use alternative treatment and providing the money.

Contents

Introduction

Hello. My name is Hazel Scade. Thank you for choosing to read 'My Pathway Through Cancer' The purpose of writing this book is to broaden your knowledge of different cancer treatments. The intention is not to substitute medical treatment. Each individual must discuss their case and course of treatment with their doctor/consultant. Introducing myself and telling you a little about my background will help to give more meaning and understanding to my experience of coping with cancer.

It has always been my ambition to help others, so after finishing my education at Wycombe High School I went straight into the nursing profession. I completed my training as a State Registered Nurse at Stoke Mandeville Hospital between the years 1972 and 1975.

I continued to work in different fields of nursing, apart from a three year maternity break, until the closure of our local hospital (Black Notley) in 1998 where I had been working as a staff nurse on an orthopaedic ward for two days a week. Unfortunately, I was unable to work the same hours in the new unit, hence the decision was made for me to leave my nursing career.

My interest in alternative approaches to health started in the early 1980's, one of the main attractions being 'the holistic approach'. Previously, my nurse's training had taken part in the days when it was routine to refer to patients by their diagnosis rather than by their name e.g. "the myocardial infarction" or "the peptic ulcer." Thankfully, this policy has changed a great deal and 'the whole person' is given much more consideration by the nursing team.

In the mid eighties, I experienced being on the receiving end of complementary therapies and my interest grew more because of the success.

Whilst studying for Developments in Nursing Care (a certificate issued by The English National Board for Nursing, Midwifery and Health

Visiting) I used it as an opportunity to consider the benefits of making complementary therapies more available in the National Health Service and then went on to qualify as a reflexology therapist in 1994.

Following further studying, I qualified for my ENB A49 Complementary Therapy for Nurses, Midwives and Health Visitors at Anglia University in 1998. This enabled me to practise massage, aromatherapy and reflexology, recognised by the N.H.S. Soon after this, I achieved a certificate for practising Reiki.

Being aware of this may help you understand the questions I was asking myself when diagnosed with advanced invasive breast cancer.

The experience has been frustrating and painful, at times, hence knowing that others must be enduring similar, or much worse, made me feel that I wanted to share some of this in order to increase one's knowledge of what is available.

According to Dr. John Briffa "Attacking Breast Cancer Naturally" Daily Mail Feb 27 2000 research has shown that up to 80% of cancer cases are believed to be preventable by using a package of lifestyle modifications. It is, therefore, my ambition to help increase one's awareness and knowledge with the aim of reducing these figures.

Whilst feeling ill, it would have been so beneficial if this sort of information was more readily available. It certainly wasn't easy to find the energy within myself and there were many times, particularly whilst receiving orthodox treatment, that I just felt like 'giving up.' However, because of this experience, it is my aim to make it easier for others by extending one's knowledge of other resources.

Being oppressed with cancer has helped me understand how close the connection is between mental thoughts and the physical body. A saying that I have used a great deal is *"Laugh and the world laughs with you. Cry and you cry alone."* Although I have never doubted it before, it now has a much stronger meaning.

Because I now feel really well (eighteen months after diagnosis) it is my desire that by reading about my insights, other people with cancer, their friends, relatives and anybody in the now myriad cancer-related health professions will be given a broader view of the experience of coping with cancer.

The Initial Diagnosis

It started on Monday April 10th 2000 when I visited my G.P. and asked him to examine my right breast. I was so sure that it wasn't anything to worry about but felt the need for some reassurance. I explained that I had visited another doctor twenty years ago with the same complaint yet was informed then that there was no need for concern.

A couple of weeks prior to this appointment a 'new client' had been to see me. Her name was Christine and she lived on the same estate as myself, yet I hadn't seen her around for a few years. She routinely filled in a consultation form. On reviewing it, I noticed she had had breast cancer and followed the orthodox routine – lumpectomy, radiotherapy and chemotherapy. This sent a shiver down my spine and made me feel that I should make an appointment with my own doctor.

For some reason I just felt the need for another check-up. However, this put my doctor in a difficult position and whilst thinking about it on the journey there, I realised that he would probably choose to refer me to the breast clinic. I said this to him and made a joke of the fact that he had better cover himself in case something should happen in the distant future as I could sue him these days! He made no comments to cause me any concern.

On leaving the surgery, he said to me *"Don't be alarmed if the appointment comes through quickly Hazel. They are very efficient in the breast clinic."* I just smiled and happily accepted his comment, then went to see a friend for a morning coffee as originally planned.

Three days later, an appointment arrived in the morning post, for the following week – April 17th. The penny did not drop that I was obviously being reviewed as an urgent case. Following my doctor's comments, I just looked upon it as good management.

I quite happily set off to the clinic by myself, taking advantage of being able to sit and read a book. My husband, Michael, had offered to escort me, but feeling that it would only be a routine visit with negative results, I said it would be a waste of his time. We all know how long one has to 'hang around' in outpatient departments!

The Infamous Mammogram

Not long after arrival at the hospital, I was referred to the mammography waiting room and took a seat. There were several of us sitting in this small room, all wearing pink robes and nursing shopping baskets with our clothes in. We all had something in common – awaiting a breast check. We probably felt like talking, but sat there with the stiff British upper lip. When I made a comment, it was just ignored.

Having a mammogram performed was a painful and unpleasant experience. I could now personally relate to those stories told to me by clients and friends.

My name was called to see the consultant. As I entered the room, three people stood at the other end and by the expressions on their faces, something told me that the news wasn't good. The consultant held out his hand and introduced himself, then the doctor who was going to take a scan of my breast and the radiographer.

I removed my gown, the consultant looked at me and commented on the difference in the shape of my breasts – I hasten to add, it appeared a lot more obvious to him than it did to me, you could just sense that he was expert in this field and had obviously seen many thousands of pairs of breasts.

Without giving me a physical examination he just told me to lie down on the couch so that an ultra scan could be taken. He would then take a needle biopsy. I looked up to the ceiling, during the procedure, and blurted out *"It's cancer isn't it?"*

Although I am unable to remember his exact reply, my comment was confirmed and he added that we would have to wait for biopsy results so that he could be more precise with my diagnosis. I got off the couch in a state of shock, held on to his arm and asked not to be left alone for too long, to which he uttered some words implying that I wouldn't be. The female radiographer kindly escorted me to a private room where she said I could remain until I felt ready to dress. That didn't appeal to me and I wanted to return to my clothing straight away, which I did.

For what seemed like eternity, I just paced up and down the corridors, (there was a choice of two) sometimes in good control, other times letting the tears flood out. I requested a glass of water on two occasions from a very pleasant W.R.V.S. lady who passed them to me with a smile. Other members of staff would also pass, obviously under quite a lot of pressure at work. Still, it would have been obvious that I was distressed, yet nobody offered assistance.

I eventually stopped a nurse from her line of duty and requested some support. Her first comment was *"You're not my patient."* I appreciated that she was probably already 'tied up' in her own field of work yet eventually, she kindly found the time and escorted me to an office. She assisted by helping to contact my husband on the telephone. I asked him to make his way over to meet me at a coffee shop in the town centre, (which had been suggested by the nurse) so that we could be together for the biopsy results from the consultant.

I was unable to relax enough to sit in a coffee bar and leaving the hospital premises appeared to be beneficial. I felt in a slightly better state of mind. Whilst waiting for Michael I called my eldest son and said that there was a delay at the hospital – blaming it on 'bad organisation.' Next, I managed to contact two of my clients that had appointments with me during the afternoon. Fortunately, for me, they were both out and I was able to leave a simple message on the answer-phone for both of them. Although

I can be rather critical about mobile telephones, for once I was pleased to be carrying one on me! I also appreciated the answer phones at the other end, because I know at that stage I would have had difficulty speaking to anybody without 'breaking down'.

Michael arrived at the car park. It was such a relief to see his car appear. However, he had to queue for a parking space. Because time was quickly ticking by, we agreed to meet back at the hospital. On arrival we met at the top of the stairs and were taken straight through to see the consultant by a lady whom I thought at that time was a secretary, yet later found out that she was the breast-care nurse. Throughout this whole time, Michael and I had been unable to converse between ourselves.

The consultant confirmed that the sample taken from my breast showed advanced breast cancer and treatment was required using chemotherapy and radiotherapy. I queried why surgery was not mentioned and he replied that the cancer was far too far advanced for that! When I asked what would happen if I refused conventional treatment I was informed that I would be dead within a year.

He said that he appreciated we were in a state of shock. The next thing to do was to speak to the breast-care nurse who would make arrangements for us to be seen in the oncology clinic in three days time.

The nurse escorted us to another room. Unfortunately, her manner appalled me! She went straight into saying that my appointment would be first thing on Thursday morning, then informed me that she was going to be away on holiday, yet if I had any queries I could leave a message on the answer phone. She then passed on a card with her name and telephone number on it, plus some leaflets showing some useful information regarding what to expect upon receiving chemotherapy and where to obtain a wig etc.

All I needed at that point was a big hug. Reassurance was also required. Wasn't it her role to do this for me? Surely she could have given some time towards helping me overcome the shock. Does this level of human empathy need to be on the syllabus? Having a nursing background myself, I still find it very difficult to understand her manner and wonder why she was appointed for the post, if this is her 'natural' character.

Although we both felt numb, my husband and I were both able to drive home in separate cars.

The next thing was to break the news to my two sons aged 14 and 10 years. This was the first day of their Easter holiday from school! Obviously, this was not at all pleasant and tears were shed. Thomas, the eldest said that it had not unduly surprised him because he had sensed 'something unpleasant' from my telephone call. Informing my parents was to be the next problem. A telephone conversation would not be adequate. We came to an agreement that Michael and I would drive ninety miles to tell them, whilst Thomas volunteered to take care of James, who had made his own plans to play with a friend.

This felt the right thing to do. I felt the need to have some time with Michael – we still had not had time alone – this would give us some time to share our thoughts on the journey there. It was also convenient being able to leave Thomas responsible for preparing a meal for James and himself to consume when needed.

As mentioned before, I was diagnosed on the first day of the Easter holiday from school. I had planned to work just for the first two days, and then would have time off with my children.

Before seeing my parents I contacted the clients that had appointments with me on Tuesday and explained the situation. Although they were shocked, great support was given to me.

When it came to telephoning my last client of the day, something told me to 'hold back.' I knew that she was going on holiday the following day and was looking forward to a back massage before her departure. On thinking about it logically, I thought to myself *"Come on Hazel. I'm no different physically than I was eight hours ago. I am still able to massage!"* I also felt I knew her well enough so that if it was obvious that I'd been crying, I'd be able to make up some excuse.

We drove to see my parents and break the news. Following their reaction, I just felt so guilty - putting other people into a state of shock. I was so used to giving comfort. This change of role just wasn't me. It felt as if I had gone into reverse gear. "You have got cancer," had been life-changing words.

Michael is a very understanding husband and was fully aware that my feelings (prior to being diagnosed) were that if ever I should develop cancer, I didn't particularly want to go along the conventional orthodox route.

On Tuesday I'm pleased to say that the massage went very well. After finishing her treatment, I left the room threw my hands up in the air with a giant grin on my face and a silent cheer. It was so therapeutic for myself as well. I'm still Hazel and able to play my role, I thought.

I went back to the room with a glass of water, treated her in the normal way, made a follow up appointment and wished her a happy holiday.

All that Christine had told me in our consultation about her breast cancer was of course in confidence. Because she lived locally, I posted a note through her letterbox explaining my situation and asked if I could tell Michael that she had also had breast cancer and that she had made a good recovery.

A few hours later, Christine knocked on the door and came in to reassure us both. Yes, the chemotherapy treatment had been quite tough going, but she had pulled through it and managed really well since then. She had continued to go to work when being treated and had even been promoted. Unfortunately though, following her quite toxic treatment, Christine had noticed another lump and because of a shadow on her spine, she had been started on Tamoxifen. This had not been effective and the treatment was changed to Arimidex.

Arimidex is a man-made, hormonal therapy type drug, used in the treatment of breast cancer on women of menopausal age and beyond. It works by interfering with the production/action of particular hormones that act as chemical messengers in the body, helping to control the activity of cells and organs. Arimidex is supposed to block this process and prevent this chemical change. It is known as an aromatase inhibitor.

Each person's reaction to the drug is unique, but the more common side-effects of this drug include hot flushes and sweats, nausea, vomiting, diarrhoea, constipation, loss of appetite, hair thinning, skin rashes, joint pain and stiffness, tiredness and lethargy. Instances of pulmonary embolism (a blood clot going to the lung) shortness of breath, cough and pharyngitis have also occurred. There is also increased risk of developing other blood clots, oedema and dizziness, as stated on www.breastdiseases.com/arimidex.htm.

All this aside, Christine was very positive. She gave Michael and myself good reassurance.

The Oncology Unit

Thursday morning arrived. We had asked my parents to come over because it had been arranged for James to play golf and we were unable to collect him now that I had an appointment with the oncologist.

As we were driving to the hospital, "The Boxer" by Simon and Garfunkel was playing on the car radio. The tears came rolling down my cheeks. This record always reminds me of my longest standing friend Margaret. Our friendship had begun over thirty years ago, even before this record was released. I can remember Margaret suffering with glandular fever and while she was recovering, she played this record in her bedroom.

It had passed through my mind that I would like a cassette made up with all my old favourites. Already, I had been having visions of lying down, feeling helpless, either recovering from cancer or travelling along the terminal path.

We arrived at the oncology clinic and I am pleased to say that we didn't have to wait too long before being seen by the consultant. He had a very pleasant manner and was very reassuring. My tumour was measured at 5.5cm x 4.5cm. The consultant explained that chemotherapy should be started as soon as possible. The treatment would last approximately 5-6 months. I could then go on to radiotherapy, after which, surgery would be considered. This would involve a total mastectomy and the lymph glands would be removed from both armpits.

I explained that this was all too much for me to take on board at that time and could only take one step at a time. Because Michael and I had had time to discuss the matter, I agreed to start chemotherapy treatment and asked if it would be allowable to receive complementary treatment – e.g. nutritional therapy, acupuncture, reflexology and aromatherapy – at the same time. He confirmed that these treatments would be of no harm and further, that some may well be of benefit.

As Monday was the day normally set aside for taking core biopsies and because the next two Mondays were going to be bank holidays, my consultant explained that chemotherapy would not be started for a fortnight. In the meantime, he would try to arrange for a core biopsy to be taken at one of the Thursday clinics instead.

This suited me fine. It meant that I would have time to adjust to it and make any arrangements that I felt necessary.

We left the clinic feeling better than we did a few days previously. I felt there was a long battle ahead and it would appear that the next year of my life was going to be focused entirely on cancer treatment.

I had come to terms with the fact that my therapy practice would have to cease temporarily. I was not only sick inside and already starting to lose weight but frightened by the crisis ahead.

On the other hand, to come through this I realised that I had to be 'ready to fight.' I was ready to face my 'new' life, ready to face reality, yet I still had a gut feeling that there was another form of treatment more suitable for me.

The next few days

The next day was Good Friday. I wrote in my diary *"Today is my 'turning' day. I have decided to make the most of it all and to feel more positive towards the changes to be made."*

I realised that there was to be no turning back and that this was going to be my greatest challenge.

I had received a lot of help and support already. Cards and letters were arriving plus flowers and telephone calls. That morning, the postman delivered our mail. One of the letters came from a client, whom I had only met a couple of months previously. He wrote *"You do have an inner energy that is transferred through your complementary practice..."* I found this a very reassuring comment that helped fuel my self-esteem. Thank you Neil!

Michael and I decided to go for a local walk, which we find relaxing. This enabled us to spend time discussing my future and how we were going to cope. I had written a note to my friend Sandra, explaining my situation and we went to deliver it.

On route we 'bumped' into Helen, a fellow therapist. I explained what had happened. She offered shiatsu treatment, hence arrangements were made for Tuesday. A big hug was the therapy for today, and so we went on.

Sandra invited us in for a coffee. We started with a general chat. Unfortunately, we had been unable to make it to her 40th birthday celebrations the week before. We took this opportunity to ask her about it and it sounded as though a good time had been had by all – what a shame we had missed it.

I then explained that although I had passed on a gift token for a full body massage, I would be unable to practise it for a while and explained the reason why. And guess what? I received a big hug. This was now an important part of my therapy. This was followed by a chat and offers of further help.

On arrival home, there were several calls on the answer-phone. One was from Halima, who had been a fellow nurse with me at the local hospital. She had been to see me the night before and practised massage on me. Now she wanted to hear about my reaction to it. Because she lives locally, I decided to go and see her.

Yes, that's right, we had a big hug! I stayed to drink a mug of hot water and have a chat. Halima informed me that she had contacted a doctor friend of hers who apparently knew the oncologist that I had seen and gave him great appraisal, which in itself was very reassuring and went towards building my confidence. I returned to Michael who had done the ironing and prepared some lunch for me.

Later that day he showed signs of being at low ebb. He decided to call Christine's husband and asked if he could have a chat. Keith is his name and he was very pleased to be of assistance. Michael went out while I stayed at home with Thomas and James.

I read some Roald Dahl to James that night. In the 'normal' routine, it was thought that he had outgrown bedtime stories and he would read to himself. However, tonight was an exception and we both enjoyed the tale. For me, it brought back childhood memories, because my home area was local to Roald Dahl's and I felt as though I recognised the surrounds he described.

I was now putting more value on the time with my family and it helped take our minds off the more serious side of life.

James settled well and I retired to bed early reading a good novel. Michael returned looking so much better and felt re-assured that there was some light at the end of the tunnel.

Saturday arrived. It was about 6.45 am and I could hear rain beating against the window pane. In the 'normal' routine Michael would have been getting ready for a game of golf with his friends. Instead, he had contacted one of them the night before and explained the situation. He appeared to be sleeping well beside me. I decided to go downstairs for a drink of water and wanted to write in my diary. It was very therapeutic for me at the time.

I was feeling that I had started to go downhill again emotionally. My lump felt a lot larger. This must have been because I had already lost weight and my bust line was always the place where I lost weight first. This had been my excuse for not dieting before. It brings back memories of my R.G.N. training days, where I had been assisting a surgeon inserting breast implants in the 'plastics' theatre. He had passed some comment that he'd do mine next if I so wished! I remember deciding that I would prefer to be 'natural'. I wonder what would have happened to my condition if I had gone ahead with that operation? Anyway, I did not have the time or energy to follow that through.

I still could not come to terms with the fact that a total mastectomy should be considered in my future. I find it difficult to put into words, yet something inside me was dreading the radical surgery more than the thought of death. Pictures of people I had nursed after foregoing radical mastectomies (this was nearly thirty years ago) came flooding back to me.

I worked on female surgery during my training days (Ward 12X and 9X Stoke Mandeville Hospital) when I was only about 18 yrs old and didn't appreciate the emotional strain one was undergoing whilst having to have a total mastectomy performed (lumpectomies, or more cosmetic surgery was not considered in those days).

Sometimes it was my role to collect the patient from theatre and receive the information that the whole breast had been removed. It wasn't always known prior to going to theatre, biopsy results, from the lump, were the deciding factor and the patient had given consent to proceed, if necessary.

Then I remember the nursing aspect e.g. a patient recovering from anaesthetic and asking if her whole breast had been removed. I would hold her hand and do my best to reassure her.

Another task was that of looking after vacuum drains left in the wound, - changing bottles and removing the drains 48hrs later, comes to mind. If I was on night duty, as a student, replacing these vacuum drains at midnight would be one of my responsibilities. I know things have progressed and this may not be necessary any longer, but I still can't wipe away the pictures of myself carrying out my role in the sluice!

I would sometimes be responsible for removing the initial dressing –large pads with strong elastopast, - the poor patient may shed a few tears, and, once again, I would hold her hand and say a few words. Wound dressings would be reviewed on a daily basis. The wound healing was recorded and reported on before finally removing the sutures or clips about ten days later.

So much of it was just looked upon as a routine task. I hope I'm wrong, and that was just my immaturity. Hopefully, the more senior staff were taking more care of the emotional aspect.

Although I felt satisfied at the time and felt that I played my role well, I now look back and realise how innocent I was. My heart goes out to you all in a different way now. I just wish that I could see you all again, it would give great support to me now telling me of your experience.

Tears are welling up in my eyes as I put this on to paper.

You are all so brave and strong. I felt that I was unable to manage the psychological and cosmetic aspect of this and would rather die instead.

However, I'm pleased to say that now I have recovered from the shock of having cancer and following research, breast surgery might be more acceptable. I would make sure that a specialist surgeon operated on me, hence improve my chances of recovery and adaptation. Also with the improvement of prosthesis over the years I know there is help at hand and have more idea of how to go about receiving it, if I don't receive it as general routine, from the hospital.

My feelings, at the time, were that cancer is a general, chronic disease. My whole self needed to be looked at – removing my breast wasn't going to eradicate other symptoms. A tumour could recur in another location.

I felt that being diagnosed with cancer was a symptom of a severely weakened immune system and that it was of more importance to restore my 'whole self' in order to destroy and eradicate these 'naughty' cancer cells. After all, my body had managed to prevent abnormal cells turning malignant for over forty years, so why couldn't I get back into balance again? Would they be able to do this under the influence of chemotherapy drugs?

I had always understood before, that in order to heal, the body should be detoxified, and then reactivated with good natural, organic food. Instead, I was going to allow a large amount of toxins to be injected into my body. I did my best to reassure myself that with the help of extra nutrients and therapies being practised on me, these would help compensate for the increase in toxicity and I would be able to make a recovery. I was not the first person to undergo this treatment was I? Thousands of others appear to have 'survived' it!

A little later Michael came downstairs and made me promise not to tire myself out. I agreed, yet still found it difficult – the thoughts of changing my lifestyle was hard to accept. However, I soon returned to bed trying to come to terms with the fact that rest was important in order for recovery to take place. I listened to a cassette that I often play as background music for my clients. This helped me relax, hence therapeutic, it also assisted towards further sleep.

During the day, I had many visitors, at different times. This included my mother and father in law, one of my sisters in law with her family, plus another friend. It was pleasant to see them all and I appreciated the interest shown. It also proved to be very tiring, repeatedly telling the same story, and remembering what I had said to whom was difficult – I feared repeating myself too much.

However, they were all very understanding and I was able to overcome the tiredness by having a short sleep between the visits.

Sunday was more relaxing. James was excited and ready to partake in the Easter egg hunt that always took place in our household on Easter Sunday. Thomas had stayed with a friend overnight and returned at 10a.m. showing some excitement on starting his hunt for 'egg-treats.'

We decided to go out for our Sunday lunch, which was pleasant. On returning home, I retired to bed for a couple of hours. I had found that a lot more rest was required. This seemed to be acceptable as a means of keeping up my strength to fight the battle and time was put aside every day for this. A 'relaxation' cassette had been purchased and this was certainly put to good use.

Michael and I both achieved the benefits from sometimes listening to it in the early hours of the morning when we had difficulty sleeping.

With further experience, it became more apparent of how important it is to find time for relaxation. I hope that from sharing this experience with you, more readers will increase their awareness and put something into practise as a preventive measure.

At approximately seven o'clock on Monday morning I wanted to rise from bed and go for a bike ride. Michael joined me…but.. Guess what? Another puncture! This had happened twice already since my diagnosis. It happened on the front wheel this time. We were at the farm by our local church. We walked home, which, I suppose, was approximately a mile.

Later, Halima came to practise acupuncture on me, whilst Michael repaired the puncture, and you'll never guess what, when he finished the repair and put the bike up the right way, he only found another puncture in the back wheel! Do you think this bike should be dumped? I definitely think it was trying to tell me something.

That afternoon we took the boys to the cinema, then on to Buckinghamshire as they were to stay with my parents. This had been arranged prior to my diagnosis because we always enjoy the change and the boys normally manage to carry out some sort of project with Grandad who is very skilled with his hands.

However, in hindsight, perhaps these were not the right plans to go along with because, obviously my parents were very shocked and couldn't help talking about me all the while. On later feedback from Thomas, he complained that they spoke over him most of the time instead of including him as a young adult. (One of the joys of learning about adolescence.) Nevertheless, we were able to talk this through and iron out the wrinkles.

Thomas was more disturbed than I originally understood and although I felt he needed to speak to somebody outside the family, he couldn't agree with any of my suggestions. I knew that there were many people he could lean on and just had to believe that things would work out alright.

When it came to the time for returning to school I spoke to the appropriate staff at both schools and felt confident that the necessary support would be given as needed.

"Children need not be excluded from this emotional upheaval – they can understand more than many people give them credit for" states Lang S. & Patt R. (1994) in 'You Don't Have to Suffer.'

Breathing Space

We were able to take advantage of the boys being occupied elsewhere. One of the errands achieved was to shop around for reclining chairs and a new sun-lounger that would be more comfortable for me whilst relaxing. This proved to be quite time-consuming and after the decision was made (for the new suite of furniture), it took a further six weeks before delivery. Nevertheless it was all worth waiting for.

It was easier to eat out, sometimes with friends. It gave relief from shopping and food preparation. I also felt more able to practise visualisation and relaxation without interfering with anybody else's plans. I still had to get used to devoting so much time towards myself.

Tuesday was a good day I remained positive and continued doing research on cancer recovery. Helen came to me as planned, and practised Shiatsu on me.

On Wednesday, Michael and I went to see our G.P. It was nine days after being diagnosed and still he had not been informed. What a poor service! However, on looking back, I do not think that he was too surprised on hearing the news. He told me to think positively which really pleased me and gave peace of mind. I felt that being on the same wavelength would go a long way towards my recuperation.

The following day I had an appointment for a core biopsy. This is a procedure where breast tissue is extracted under local anaesthetic, then sent to the laboratory for further analysis. It pleased me to find that the nurse, whom I had seen before, played her role much more to my approval. She held my hand and gave reassurance during the procedure. It helped me feel that our preliminary meeting must have been on one of her 'off' days.

However, unfortunately, this was the only time, in my opinion, that she played her role satisfactorily, because I made further telephone calls and was very displeased with her response.

As an example, after leaving a request for test results on her answer phone, she would just leave messages on mine such as "that information is in your notes and I can't get hold of them." I know that when I have been in similar positions, during my career as a nurse in hospital, it may have meant extra time and effort yet I would never have left a patient 'in the air' like that.

She never put any effort into speaking to me personally, such as telling me what time would be more suitable for a telephone conversation, or could she have arranged a visit? I don't know if she was able to do call outs, if not, perhaps she could have arranged an appointment for me to go there. If that wasn't possible, surely she could have put me into contact with *somebody* that could pass on information and reassure me. I felt desperate at the time – almost *anybody* would have done. Couldn't she understand that?

The next couple of days were spent shopping and socialising, with relaxation and reading in between times.

Sunday, Michael drove to Buckinghamshire to collect the boys. I stayed at home to rest and reserve my energy for the treatment that was going to start the following week.

When they arrived home, James presented me with a heart shaped piece of wood with the words "Mummy and Daddy I love you" which he had made for me as a good luck token.

My father later informed me that this was totally his own idea. He had approached Grandad and just asked for the materials with which to do it. Thomas had also given some assistance with 'trying to get it right'.

I was later presented with these photographs and from that day on the heart has hung in my bedroom.

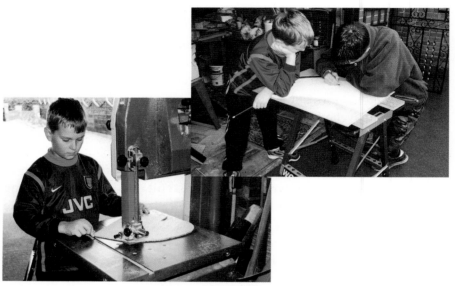

"Thank-you boys."

Chemotherapy begins

It was the evening before my chemotherapy was to be administered. Both boys were out and Michael and I decided to go for another cycle ride. Yes, the bike has remained puncture-free for a while now. Whilst out for this ride, I asked him to hold my hand at the same time as cycling. Of course, being Michael, this embarrassed him, but we managed and it brought smiles to our faces as it does even now just thinking about it.

I am very grateful to my husband he has given very good support all the way through. I love him lots!

Chemotherapy day had now arrived. Having been informed of the fact that because of the high dose of drugs vomiting was going to occur, I made arrangements for James to stay with a friend that night. Thomas, being older and with a different nature would be alright in the house.

The appropriate drugs were administered to me intravenously at three o'clock that afternoon.

The oncology team believe this to be the most effective way of wiping out a large amount of cancer cells. This highly toxic fluid that was being injected into my veins would burn the skin if just a tiny drip came into contact with it! For this reason, the nurse administering it was protected by wearing gloves and needed to be very safety conscious. I couldn't help but ask myself *"If such precautions need to be taken outside, what is it doing to me, inside?"* Nobody would talk much about the side effects. Would they remain permanent? Does harm vary from patient to patient depending on sex, age, general health and one's attitude towards it? I suppose only time could tell.

I was also aware that being a 'cancer patient' was starting to rule my life because of appointments for 'this and that' (my dear Michael was also escorting me all the time). However, my adamant determination and nursing experience was not going to let this happen. I vowed that I was not going to have hypochondria! My aim was to remain as human as possible.

I had determined that the next nine to twelve months was only going to be a small part of my life.

We arrived home with me feeling no different and not sure what to expect. I had taken some precautions against vomiting i.e. received acupuncture, had consumed ginger for forty-eight hours and had applied pressure pads to the appropriate points on both wrists.

Although the affects of these may be unproven I was going by my past experience in the complementary line, advice that had been given by other colleagues, and articles in numerous books and magazines that I have read in the past, about acupressure relieving nausea. At least I felt satisfied that I had put some effort into taking precautions.

A book written by Suzannah Olivier entitled "The Breast Cancer Prevention and Recovery Diet" (1999) states "Ginger or peppermint tea, either on their own or in combination, are very helpful for reducing nausea induced by chemotherapy. In trials ginger has been shown to be as effective as anti-nausea pills for travel sickness and morning sickness and it is a great boon for chemotherapy-induced nausea."

So, it was definitely worth a try, wasn't it?

I consumed a bread roll with a glass of water a couple of hours following treatment then just sat down to rest and tried to read, without much success. Vomiting started at approx. 7p.m. and was still with me thirty-six hours later! I couldn't even keep down a sip of water!

The morning following the chemotherapy administration, I received a 'routine' 'phone call from an oncology nurse who wasn't surprised to hear that I was vomiting and reassurance was given. However, following a further twenty-four hours of this, I felt rather drained.

As soon as the oncology dept. opened I telephoned to speak to a nurse who suggested that I contact my own G.P. and request a prescription for stronger anti-emetics. Michael did this for me. My doctor was more than willing to write the prescription, for the suggested two drugs, and Michael went to collect them. Now the hassle started. He visited every chemist in town, yet none of them stocked one of the drugs – it was very expensive, so I suppose not often prescribed.

At approximately 10.00 a.m. he arrived home with one of them, for me to administer, rectally, which, I am pleased to say had some of the desired effect.

Whilst I was doing this, Michael contacted the hospital pharmacy for advice. They informed him that the second drug should be ready for dispense at about 2 p.m.

At 12.30 p.m. my family doctor visited and confirmed that I was dehydrated and if anti-emetics didn't have the desired effect, I would have to be admitted to hospital. However I informed him that I had noticed some improvement since the administration of the new drug a couple of hours previously.

Michael received a call, informing him that the drug was now available for collection from the hospital. Obviously, this tablet was administered as soon as he arrived home. Half an hour later, I was able to take sips of water without vomiting! Perhaps, I was trying to progress a bit too fast, because when I tried to consume some soup at 7 p.m. it soon came back up! Anyway, I was still happy with being able to drink water. Later Dioralyte (an oral electrolyte replacement and rehydration solution) was added and achieved the desired effect.

The day following I felt much improved, hence was able to put more effort towards sprucing myself up. I showered and washed my hair, chose bright summery clothing to wear and applied some make up. However, this seemed to sap up my energy and I had to lie down for another couple of hours to recuperate.

Nausea was still present and I had to continue with medication. Vomiting would sometimes occur, yet there was no comparison with how I felt 48 hours earlier.

I originally thought that whilst undergoing this treatment I would just need to rest and this would be an opportunity to catch up with reading and letter writing that I never seem to find time for in the normal routine. However, I was wrong. It didn't turn out to be anything like that.

My life could so easily have come to a halt. My body demanded more sleep, yet I still did not wake refreshed. Any literature read or other people's experience did not convey the physical reality of what was happening in my body.

I feel that this is where I am very fortunate to have experience of complementary therapies and to be moving in a circle where receiving treatment was reasonably easy. Special thanks goes out to all those people who so kindly offered their services. In fact, I was so inundated with them that not everybody was able to share their willingness. Even people I had never met before heard about me and offered time and help.

It so happened that two spiritual healers who lived locally were amongst those who came forward. I had never experienced spiritual healing before and knew very little about it. I must say that I found it a very pleasant experience. On one occasion I wrote in my diary *'the experience was quite ecstatic and very powerful.'* These two people were kind enough to see me on a weekly basis over a long period of time. Besides other therapists practising massage, reflexology, acupuncture, shiatsu and reiki on me, I was able to receive therapeutic treatment approximately four or five times a week.

These treatments all helped with the relaxation aspect of my treatment.

Five days following my chemotherapy treatment, a Macmillan nurse came to visit me. She was excellent. She started by greeting me with a big hug, then went on to provide further information as to what to expect from the proposed treatment.

She warned me that I was in for a 'rough' time and would generally get a lot weaker as chemotherapy treatment advanced. She also prepared me for not being able to walk far (knowing that this was something Michael and I enjoyed together) and I was to come to terms with doing less over the next couple of months.

At the same time, she was very positive thinking and wanted to support me 100%. She kindly gave advice on things like diet and hair loss, leaving a turban made of towelling and said she would send some different colours, which, of course she did.

Michael was present at the time. She included him in all the conversation and offered to make arrangements for further counselling for him, Thomas and James, if needed.

Before leaving, she left useful information leaflets, her card, with a telephone number that I could contact at any time (a message could be left if she wasn't available) and made a follow-up appointment to see me again.

The Macmillan Cancer Relief team was started back in 1911, the aim being to increase public awareness and the ability to cope with cancer. M.C.R. was started by Douglas Macmillan who had helplessly watched his own father die of cancer.

This nurse certainly carried out her role very well and helped give a realistic approach towards my outlook. I also felt that it was a career that I would like to follow when my health would allow.

The general service was excellent. Good response was given to all 'phone calls and enquiries made.

As the time was approaching to have my second course of treatment, I was feeling at a very low ebb. Something inside me was saying, *"This just doesn't feel right."* Since receiving my first treatment, I had frequent 'cold' symptoms i.e. runny nose and sore throat plus a feeling of general listlessness. I find it hard to describe my mental state – I just felt generally flattened. Nothing much seemed to penetrate my dead-headedness. At times, I did not really care about anything; I was not me any more. I was no longer inside my physical body. In some way perhaps, I was hoping that my blood results would not be suitable for a second course, and then this would delay treatment for a while. I just had to wait and see.

Although I never meant it to, my feelings were being reflected and other people noticed. It became apparent that James had shed tears without me being aware. I approached him and did my best to give reassurance, obviously with big hugs. I know Thomas was finding it difficult as well, yet communication between us was a problem.

New Looks

Another chore that I had to endure was purchasing a wig. My hair had started to fall out. My regular hairdresser had been very caring and supportive. She had given me a wig on loan. However, because Michael and my parents didn't think it looked much like the 'normal' me and I had the chance to purchase a wig at a reduced rate via the N.H.S., I thought I should at least see what else was available. I therefore contacted a hairdresser who was able to offer this service. Following a pleasant telephone conversation, an appointment was booked and after making arrangements for Thomas and James, Michael and I made our way to the salon. Because it entailed an hour's journey to the coast, we tried to make it as enjoyable as possible.

The hairdresser was a courteous and considerate man, also named Michael. He gave a great deal of advice on the care of wigs as he put many different ones on my head. I chose one that Michael thought looked most like my original head of hair.

Now, with two different styled wigs, my intentions were to make the most of being able to change my appearance so easily and always have nice looking hairstyles. Unfortunately, however, it never worked out that way, because at a later date, when I had no hair, it wasn't comfortable to wear a wig, neither did I feel in the right frame of mind to want to go to that much trouble or discomfort, very often.

Following this appointment Michael and I went down to the sea front for a nice long walk. My diet rules were broken, yet I enjoyed consuming a 'Magnum' ice cream whilst walking.

Some parts of our visit that day saddened me. Our last visit to this area had been five months prior when James celebrated his tenth birthday. He had chosen to take his friend Sam to a go-kart track not far from there. Because it was such a lovely sunny day we were able to go for a walk and visit the local amusement fairground. Whilst walking, we could not help but reminisce – little did we know then, that we would be returning to the area in such unforeseen circumstances.

However, I am pleased to say that a reasonably positive attitude was adopted and we returned to collect James with smiles on our faces whilst able to make a joke of my 'new look'. Thomas returned later in the evening and also approved of the wig.

Two days before my next appointment, I heard something being posted through the letterbox, whilst resting, yet did not take much notice. When I felt ready, I went and picked it up and must say that reading the contents gave me a new burst of energy. It was some information from the Internet about the Cancer Alternative Information Bureau (C.A.I.B.).

A few days prior, Alison, another nursing colleague, had visited me with Halima, when she came to practise acupuncture on me. During the course of the conversation, I had explained that I had been trying to contact this organisation and Alison thought it sounded vaguely familiar to something she had seen on the Internet and hey presto this was it.

On reading the literature, it just so happened that there was going to be a seminar held in London two weeks later.

When Michael arrived home, I passed on the information and he agreed that we should definitely follow it through further. Later, when he sat down to read it in more detail, he agreed that it was clearly worth considering going out to Mexico for less hostile treatment. All this appeared to give me more strength to go to the oncology clinic two days later. I had some sort of feeling that this might be my last time!

My blood results were satisfactory; hence, the same intravenous chemotherapy drugs were dispensed. This time, the anti-emetic drug that had been effective following the last treatment, was also administered intravenously.

I am pleased to say that the vomiting was less, yet still bad enough. I felt that my life had come to a halt. I did my best to put on a good act to all those around me but still felt very different inside. All hours of the day, I felt quite listless. My sense of taste was strange. There was a metallic taste in my mouth for the first few days following treatment accompanied by a furry feeling on my teeth, not alleviated with brushing or mouthwashes. This reminded me that not only were cancer cells being destroyed but also the soft tissue in my mouth and throat. Foods simply lost flavour. I could no longer enjoy consuming food and drink.

Preparing meals, eating, entertaining and dining out had always been an important part of my lifestyle, and I needed the nutritional value to assist recovery. Taking this away from me felt like a dark, deep hole being dug in front of me.

This is where my mother was very helpful. On a weekly basis, she would come to see me with my father and would always be laden down with prepared food. She had purchased 'Healing Foods Cookbook' from The Bristol Cancer Help Centre (B.C.H.C.) and did very well preparing new recipes with many ingredients she had never heard of before. She would sometimes prepare meat dishes for the rest of my family too.

Following this diet wasn't difficult for me, because I had favoured eating vegetarian for many years. It was just to make it easier to 'fit in' with others that I would eat fish and although I did my best to avoid dairy products they would sometimes be included. I would sometimes really enjoy eating cheese. Now however, it seemed to be important to eat vegan.

Margaret, my 'old' friend from church choir days more than thirty years ago, whom I mentioned earlier, now runs a small catering business. She frequently provides lunch and makes soup for her customers. When making anything suitable for me, in my condition, she would make extra and freeze it for me in small containers. Because I only felt able to consume a very soft diet for about a week following chemotherapy, this was very helpful.

Photography is one of my father's interests and he would nearly always carry his camera when visiting. I would sometimes pose for photographs, which could be therapeutic. It also gave me some pleasure making up an album that could be referred to, either for personal reminiscence or to show others.

During this treatment my stamina was affected. I found that even when resting, I was unable to concentrate to read a book, do a crossword or write a letter.

This was no way to live. What was the point? To make matters worse I was losing my hair by the handful. It was continually falling out and leaving a trail. Having a shower was now unpleasant – instead of feeling clean and refreshed I was just covered with hair. I had to spend an extra five minutes brushing it off me and cleaning out the shower tray.

It was all just so difficult. Although life around me had to continue as normal, I could sense that others who knew the situation were behaving differently and keeping an eye on me.

Many people did not know how to approach me. Embarrassment showed on their faces and they would even cross the road, pretending not to see me. I could even sense people looking at me whilst trying to weigh up if I really looked like a person with cancer. For this reason I almost found it easier when my hair fell out – then people could see that there was something wrong with me.

My emotions would change from high to low. One moment I would be euphoric, appreciating the role of living and being loved, then I could sink down into a dark pit when the side effects of treatment would impede my ego and remind me that I had a serious illness. These mood swings also made it difficult for my family. They were sometimes shocked by my elation, and did not know how to deal with it. If I was depressed, it would appear that this is what most people expected of me. Many would say that I should be grateful for being diagnosed; otherwise, it might have been too late. I should have been pleased to receive treatment.

I felt particularly sorry for my two sons. It was difficult enough for them trying to accept the fact that I had cancer. My mood swings must have made it more difficult because they hadn't had enough experience of life to fully understand this.

In my diary I would often write that I was feeling depressed, feeling that there was no easy way out. Knowing that I wasn't that close to death, there didn't appear to be an easy alternative. If I had to continue along this path, my inner feelings told me that I had the strength to fight, yet still felt that the treatment needed should not be so uncomfortable.

Seeing a light at the end of the tunnel that I was trying hard to stretch out to helped towards giving me some power of endurance. I felt sure that being diagnosed with cancer was for a particular purpose. Could it be to try and open the doors to less invasive treatment being made more available on the N.H.S.?

Six weeks on

It was now about six weeks since my initial diagnosis. Conventional treatment had continued, with complementary therapists working alongside me. The shock of the diagnosis now seemed to have lifted and I was more able to think about my health and myself.

Cancer wasn't my first illness. It must have developed for a reason. All sorts of thoughts ran through my head. Could my cancer have occurred in order for me to use my personal power responsibly and wisely? I felt that I had to learn to love myself more instead of giving it all to others. I also needed to show others the ability to fight this dreaded illness and to prove that our bodies are meant to heal themselves.

I have had a fair amount of medical treatment during my lifetime. My interest in 'different' treatments, i.e. those not always offered by the N.H.S. started over seventeen years ago. Then, approximately sixteen years ago I sought help from a 'natural healing doctor' for back problems, with great success. He was the person who made me more aware of my own body and understood what I meant when I referred to 'inner feelings.' He suggested that I should 'listen' and perhaps be guided by them more often.

About six years prior to my diagnosis, one of my aunts was diagnosed with breast cancer. When Mum told me about her treatment and progress I said, *"If ever that should happen to me Mum I think I would go along an alternative path first."* Mum responded, *"That's all very well for you to say now. But I bet if it happened to you, your attitude would change!"* I had also made similar comments to my husband. Now the time had come, my body really did want to go along another route – Mum was wrong- my attitude had not changed.

After my initial G.P appointment I had decided to call the Bristol Cancer Help Centre and explain that although I hadn't been diagnosed with cancer I wanted to have some information about the centre 'just in case.'

Following my diagnosis, the information from the centre was of great interest. Michael and I thought it would be beneficial to go to an introductory course in order to meet other people in similar situations and to improve Michael's knowledge of the meaning of the 'holistic' approach. Because we also thought it would be advantageous for me to go on the residential course, Michael wanted to have a 'taste' of what the centre was like in order to be with me more, spiritually, whilst we were apart.

I was hoping that although the aim of B.C.H.C. appeared to be working alongside the N.H.S. to provide integrated care, somebody there would understand that I wanted to follow a different pathway.

Looking back at the diary I kept, whilst ill, on Tuesday 25th April, just eight days following initial diagnosis, all I had written was " *A good day today I remain positive and have continued making plans and doing research towards a 'natural' recovery.*"

So, you see, for some reason I just was not feeling happy with the conventional route.

Approximately one year later, I read the book "Cancer, Why We Are Still Dying to Know The Truth". Phillip Day writes *"The key to stopping the cancer growth doesn't lie in traditional treatments like chemo and radiation therapy or surgery, but in an approach that works with the body instead of against it."*

The Seminar

It was Monday June 5th 2000. A seminar, organised by the Cancer Alternative Information Bureau, was being held in London.

Although there were a few hitches along the way, I eventually managed to obtain tickets for Michael and I to attend. Arrangements were made for both boys to stay with friends whilst we went to London for a couple of days.

On listening to the different speakers, I definitely felt that this was more like the path that I wanted to follow and whilst eating our evening meal, following the first day of speakers, Michael agreed with me whole-heartedly.

The experience of this day was a reinforcement of previous research I had carried out which had shown how scientist after scientist had urged that continuing with present lines of conventional treatment could only mean going from crisis to catastrophe. I had read about the possibilities of conventional treatment being largely exhausted and that no further worthwhile progress could be expected from such measures.

There appeared to be an urgent need for the disease to be tackled from a different approach.

Further facts stated by the C.A.I.B. that confirmed my inner feelings are:

- There is strong evidence to suggest that cancer is a disease of the immune system. A strong immune system is the key to fighting and controlling this disease.
- There are two basic principles to follow in the non-conventional treatment of cancer:
  a) Detoxify the body
  b) Build up the immune system

With both these principles in place it is believed you can fight the disease.

In a handout, given at the seminar dated 5-15-2000 and entitled "Complementary and Alternative Medicine Approaches to Cancer – 2000: Key Concepts", Dr Michael Schachter stated: *"Conventional medicine focuses on destroying cancerous tumours with surgery, radiation and chemotherapy without much attention being paid to the body's natural defences against cancer."*

My inner feelings had been saying to me, *"Don't attack this cancer. Instead, you should be restoring good cells in your immune system which will automatically 'take over' the cancer cells."* I cannot forget being taught in my nurse's training that our immune system is the body's major line of defence, so that when threatened by foreign organisms known as 'pathogens,' this system is able to produce a supply of antibodies in order to fight back. My gut feeling was that this system should be able to recognise 'bad' cells and destroy them. I needed to build up my supply of 'good' cells to go into battle.

Another form of Dr Schachter's treatment was to intravenously administer vitamin C to aid in the killing of cancerous cells. This supported other articles I had read previously, one of them being in the book Cancer and Nutrition published by B.C.H.C. October 1996 by Dr. Rosy Daniel and Dr. Sandra Goodman It states: *"It is thought that Vitamin C slows down or stops the growth of malignant cells by inhibiting the action of hyaluronidase - the substance necessary for cell division, proliferation and migration. In some centres, dosages of Vitamin C as high as 25 grams per day are taken for brief periods when cancer is active. This comes close to using Vitamin C as a form of chemotherapy."*

Different studies have shown that vitamin C has the ability to decrease oestrogen-induced tumour growth. Therefore, in cases of oestrogen-dependent breast cancer (my diagnosis), vitamin C will lower the concentration of toxic hormonal substances produced by oestrogens.

There is also another article of interest, about this subject, in *The Cancer Handbook – What's Really Working, written and* edited by Lynne Mc Taggart First published in various editions of **What Doctors Don't Tell You** Vol. 1-7 between 1990 and 1997 tells the story of the publisher's 81year old mother who was diagnosed with breast cancer that was too far advanced to perform chemotherapy or any other intervention, leading to tamoxifen and morphine being prescribed.

She was taken to a Dr. Patrick Kingsley, who believes that cancer can be treated with very large doses of vitamin C and other antioxidants. A strict exclusion diet was prescribed i.e. avoid junk food, dairy products and some grains (particularly wheat). Initially intra-venous infusions of vitamin C and other nutrients were administered twice a week, gradually reducing to once every six weeks. Following this regime, with no other orthodox intervention, a complete recovery was made – lumps disappeared and ulcers healed.

Some doctors also believe that large doses of vitamin C can encourage the production of interferon. This is a protein produced by the white blood cells, which can act as a weapon against the abnormal cancer cells.

Linda Lazarides (1996) quotes in her book ' Nutritional Therapy' "In the late 1970's Pauling teamed up with a Scottish physician Ewan Cameron to treat terminal cancer patients with ten grams of vitamin C at The Vale of Leven Hospital. Although the results of the trial were very encouraging, with several of the patients surviving for many years after the dates predicted for their death, most of the medical establishment resisted Cameron and Pauling's efforts to repeat the study using larger numbers of patients, and the whole subject became extremely controversial."

At a later date, I decided to increase my intake of vitamin C, yet when I took a list of the vitamins I was taking to my G.P. and asked what could be prescribed on the N.H.S. he said he could try giving me a prescription for vitamin C. However, his computer rejected the high dose. He therefore gave me a hand written prescription.

I was only to find that two different chemists also told me that the computer rejected it because of the 'high dose' that was required. They were unable to satisfy my needs.

Once again, I had to put my hand in my pocket and purchase vitamin C myself. How can this be fair? The same computer didn't mind the pharmacist dispensing other drugs for me that were a lot more expensive and more toxic to my system (the anti-sickness ones that my husband had difficulty finding cost about £150, to see me over one session of chemotherapy, in comparison with a month's supply of vitamin C costing £14.)

I also appreciate that although vitamin C has extremely low toxicity, even at high doses, there is a possibility that gastric distress, such as gas and bloating can occur. However, I did read in "An Alternative Medicine Definitive Guide to Cancer" (1997) that a nutritional biochemist Ross Pelton states, "this problem can be alleviated by switching to the less acidic calcium ascorbate salt."

Detoxification is always important and supported by all speakers and writers in this field.

"Hormonal imbalance often needs attention in breast cancer patients." was another fact that Michael Schachter stated. Once again, this supported my own inner feelings and applied to me. Changes that I had noticed within myself were thought to be 'menopausal symptoms.'

Approximately twelve years before my cancer diagnosis, I had investigations carried out for secondary infertility problems, which had shown low progesterone levels. Several years later, I decided to apply natural progesterone cream, yet for no particular reason discontinued using it. Now I felt that I wanted to put it into operation again and on consultation with my doctor he confirmed that it would be alright to do so.

I later read about an eighteen-year research programme that had been carried out in Guy's Hospital, London showing that women with breast cancer who were treated with natural progesterone had twice the survival rates of those who had not. Patrick Holford and Kate Neil in Balancing Hormones Naturally (1998) state this was reported in the British Journal of Cancer, January 1996.

Dr. John Lee and many others support the use of natural progesterone for breast cancer.

In his book, "Natural Progesterone" (1996) Dr. Lee writes, "The point of this brief detour is that low premenopausal progesterone as a consequence of anovulatory cycles can induce increased oestrogen levels and lead to symptomatically significant oestrogen dominance prior to menopause. The most common age for breast or uterine cancer to originate is five years before menopause (though it may not be diagnosed for eight to ten years)".

D.H.E.A. (dehydro-epi-andosterone) was also mentioned. This is a hormone produced by the adrenal glands as well as the brain and skin. We should produce large quantities of D.H.E.A. in comparison with other hormones. In turn it is converted into oestrogen. Although it is a little tricky, some studies indicate that if a woman has high serum levels of D.H.E.A., she has less risk of developing breast cancer.

"Definitive Guide to Cancer" (1997) by W. John Diamond and W. Lee Cowden with Burton Goldberg states "Low D.H.E.A. levels can leave one vulnerable to breast, prostrate and bladder cancer," then goes on to say that "Dr. Stretch of the Institute of Complementary Medicine in Seattle, Washington notes that premenopausal women with low circulating levels of D.H.E.A. tend to have a higher incidence of breast cancer."

"The Super Hormone Promise (1996) by W. Regelson and C. Coleman states "D.H.E.A. supplementation in their food prevented breast cancer in a strain of female mice that are prone to die of it."

In my case, on a later date, I had a blood test showing my level was very low, hence I started on an average dose of D.H.E.A. and further tests have shown improvement. (I will say a little more about this hormone later on).

Back to the conference. Michael Schachter spoke about many more predisposing factors towards cancer, explaining that four of these agents have to be present to cause malignancy. Our cells are able to tolerate three 'foreign bodies' (see appendix 1) yet when a fourth one enters abnormal cell division, known as mutation, becomes apparent. This encourages a cancer growth. Because the immune response is low, the body is unable to deal with it and cancer growth takes over.

I found it reassuring to have confirmation that several factors go towards the development of cancer. Somehow, this appears to help alleviate my feelings of guilt from having cancer diagnosed. Although I still feel that, in some ways, many major illnesses are self-induced, I still feel unable to detect the root cause of cancer becoming apparent in me.

Because I also believe that it is the root, which needs to be treated, I hoped that making a few changes in my lifestyle would be adequate.

Michael Schachter's clinic takes a comprehensive approach, emphasizing a health-promoting diet and lifestyle, in which toxins from foods and the environment are eliminated as much as possible. Natural substances are also administered, either orally or in an injectable form.

He divides his dietary guidelines into two sections – foods to eat and foods to avoid. The avoidance list included alcohol, coffee, white flour and sugar, food additives, pesticides, fluoridated water and all fluoride-containing products, such as toothpaste, hydrogenated fats and foods with added aluminium products.

Aluminium cookware and antiperspirant deodorants containing aluminium should also be avoided.

A diet with low to moderate fat content, high fibre, moderate to high-complex-carbohydrate and moderate protein centred around whole grains, fresh fruit and vegetables, a modest amount of nuts, seeds, fish and poultry (all of organic range if possible) is what he recommended. If tolerated, he suggested aiming for 50% of this being raw.

In all cases, Dr.Schacter's dietary principle is flexible. He aims to help his clientele on an individual basis with the aim of doing well. If signs of decline occur, dietary modifications are suggested, which based on his clinical experience, may be of value.

He also generally prescribes vitamins and minerals because cancer patients have shown evidence of deficiency in this line.

Like many of the other speakers at the conference, Dr Schachter also supported using complementary therapies as a means of improving the body defences against cancer.

Dr. Schachter states in "Definitive Guide to Cancer" 1997 *"It is important to help the patient reframe the cancer experience as a message that one's life is not in harmony or balance and that changes in lifestyle would be helpful."*

Another thing, I felt of some relevance to me that Dr. Schachter mentioned was a connection between wearing bras and breast cancer. Apparently following a three year study there was some evidence that women who wore their bras 12 hrs daily (I think he said particularly underwired ones) were 21 times more likely to develop breast cancer than those who do not wear bras that long. If women wore their bra 24 hours a day this figure went up six-fold, which meant that those who wore bras all the time had a 125-fold greater risk of developing breast cancer than those who refrained from wearing one at all.

I never followed this with any great research, yet read in Professor Jane Plant's book "Your Life in Your Hands" (2000) "Nor do I think that the factors such as using mobile 'phones, deodorants or wearing incorrectly fitting bras cause breast cancer. Breast cancer has been a feature of western societies long before these relatively modern inventions. Clearly, we should not wear bras that are too small to the extent that they stop circulation, but do women, especially middle-class go round wearing such tight bras?"

Suzannah Olivier, in The Breast Cancer book 1999, also writes a small section on the subject, advising one to purchase well-fitting bras that do not constrict any breast tissue and precludes under-wired ones.

Rachel Charles, in "Mind, Body and Spirit" refers to the same research as Dr. Schachter referred to and advises one to wear loose clothing in order to allow the lymph drainage system to do its job unimpeded.

This has increased my awareness, yet, being in the lower end of the statistics mentioned, I felt there wasn't any need to make any great relevant changes.

Gilberto Alvarez, a doctor from Mexico, told us of his clinical experience of more than twenty years and how satisfactory results had been shown in the treatment of cancer using natural methods and nutritional support, along similar lines as Dr. Schachter

Dr. Ralph Moss also inspired me when questioning chemotherapy. He informed us of an apparently known fact that every year more and more people with cancer are treated with chemotherapy. Is it safe? Is it effective? Is it necessary? These were some questions he put forward before going on to answer them by telling us about his research.

He stated that 'knowledge is power' and informed us that he had a book published, (Questioning Chemotherapy) which to his knowledge was the first book written for the general public. His primary focus for more than twenty years had been to educate patients about legitimate and innovative cancer therapies. Obviously, I have purchased this book, which has proved to be very useful towards my further research.

Under the heading of one of the drugs used on me for chemotherapy treatment, it stated that damage to the heart muscle could be one of the side effects even after low dosage. I thought that I would probably fall into this category. Did I really want to take the risk? It also stated that doctors would monitor the heart carefully when this drug was administered, yet I wasn't aware of this being done for me.

At the end of this two-day seminar, a lady from the audience went on stage to tell us of her experience. Sarcomas had been apparent all over her skeleton, particularly down the spine. She had been told that there was no more treatment for her and had to start taking large doses of morphine for pain relief, a year prior to when she was speaking. As a last resort, she was escorted to New York in a wheelchair to see Dr Schachter who administered nutritional infusions. She was pleased to announce that great improvements were made – within a fortnight she had reduced (or finished) taking morphine and returned to England being able to walk again and look after herself independently.

At the time of talking, she was in the process of starting a supportive complementary cancer group in her area.

Thanks to the C.A.I.B., this two-day seminar had been very inspirational to both Michael and myself.

Although we had originally thought that I would be going to America for treatment, following discussions with other people during coffee/lunch breaks and cards/leaflets we had collected, we thought it sensible to start by having consultations in this country.

Attending this seminar however had taken all the stamina out of me. I was languid and needed to rest for a couple of days.

After reading the literature we had collected, we decided to make appointments with two of the doctors that advertised, one in London and one in Kent. All this would be following my time in Bristol.

Bristol Cancer Help Centre

It was only a few days before we went to the Bristol Cancer Help Centre. We had also been informed that because it was the centre's twentieth year celebration, Prince Charles, being the Centre's Patron, would be present during our stay.

By the time we arrived at the centre, we had both agreed that the quality of my future life was important and going on the figures of recovery being so minimal, there seemed little point in continuing with the current treatment.

The two-day introductory course proved to be beneficial to both of us. It felt so nice to be in a haven of peace and tranquillity. Everybody was so considerate. It felt like one big family, sharing feelings with others in similar positions. I met people whom I felt were in a worse condition than myself, and others who have been down similar pathways before, who were able to lift my spirits and help build strength towards fighting for the future.

The importance of receiving certain complementary therapies was confirmed. Relaxation remained an important factor. Meditation was introduced and would be practised on a daily basis – the goal being to give the brain a period of total rest. Doctors have proven that people who meditate on a regular basis are less stressful, have stronger immune systems and are generally healthier.

Dr. Alec Forbes, was Bristol Cancer Help Centre's first Medical Director, and, according to Pat Pilkington, the co-founder "He studied and practised spiritual healing and transpersonal psychology, looking beyond symptoms to the underlying causes of disease. He felt that science, in focussing ever more minutely on the disease process, was missing the potential for self-healing.

He travelled widely looking at alternative, non-toxic metabolic therapies that viewed cancer as a systemic disease brought about by modern lifestyles. He lectured extensively at home and abroad and wrote widely on the subject of nutrition" as stated in B.C.H.C.'s newsletter Spring 2000.

Bernie Siegel (a retired surgeon) gives further support to this. In Love, Medicine and Miracles (1986) he writes "The physical benefits of meditation have recently been well documented by Western medical researchers, notably Dr. Herbert Benson. It tends to lower or normalize blood pressure, pulse rate, and the levels of stress hormones in the blood. It produces changes in brain wave patterns, showing less excitability. These physical changes reflect changes in attitude, which show up on psychological tests as a reduction in the over competitive Type A behaviour that increases the risk of heart attack. Meditation also raises the pain threshold and reduces one's biological age. Its benefits are multiplied when combined with regular exercise. In short, it reduces wear and tear on both body and mind, helping people live better and longer."

In the '1997 Alternative Medicine Definitive Guide to Cancer', it is written *"Many physicians now believe that treating an individual's mental and emotional states is as important as treating any cancerous tumours that may be a result of such conditions."*

Some of the aims listed for this residential course, at Bristol, are:-

- Introducing the role of the mind in affecting the physiology of the body and future life and illness outcomes.
- An exploration of personal goals, dreams and ambitions with encouragement and support, enabling you to achieve these and help in regaining a strong sense of 'self.'
- To examine the use of illness as an opportunity for deepening your self-awareness, and to find new meaning, value and purpose in life, so you can come to live contentedly in the present.
- To deepen your understanding and use of meditation, visualisationand relaxation.
- To enjoy rest and recovery.

I am pleased to say that I achieved all of these.

On return from the centre I made sure that I would sink into my pillow, concentrate on my breathing and attune to the subtleties of my inner world, on a daily basis, with the aim of practising it at least three times a day.

I would visualise my cancer as a nasty black mass of earth. A gardening figure would then appear with a fork and would work hard to break this mound of earth into smaller pieces. Fertiliser and nutrients would then be added before planting flower seeds. Next, I could see lovely colourful flowers growing. This is how it was going to be for me. My cancer mass was reducing in size anyway. It was going to continue like this and soon the flowers would be in full bloom!

Another form of relaxation was to visualise myself on a Caribbean Island. I could see myself on a small island laying under a palm tree to shade from the sun, which was present in the lovely blue sky, whilst the waves just lapped against the shoreline of golden sand.

This really worked well for me. I was able to feel warm and relaxed, hence allowing my body to function in tranquillity.

Dr. Etienne Callebout, M.D. who practises in Harley Street, London studied the problem of cancer in great depth following his father's death from it. He states (1997) "To cope with their emotions the cancer patient must be given a structured programme of self-care including for example, meditation, guided imagery and autosuggestion, including the use of self-statements, such as: 'My legs and arms are becoming warm and heavy, all the muscles in my body are softening and melting, deep relaxation runs through my body.' Numerous case reports exist demonstrating 'spontaneous remission' of cancers in people practicing meditation in the absence of conventional treatment. I try to guide my patients in developing ways to induce present-moment awareness, a state of relaxed yet focused attention, a peaceful, non-judgmental frame of mind."

The senior chef, who was the author of the cookbook previously mentioned, gave an interesting lecture on the importance of a well balanced diet. She expressed the importance of avoiding food that was difficult to digest because this would mean wasting energy plus valuable minerals, vitamins and enzymes during the process instead of using them more efficiently towards stimulating the immune system to enhance the healing process. This power is gained by eating a nutritious diet, free of animal and dairy products, saturated fats, sugar and additives.

An additional reason for avoiding meat and dairy products is the fact that they contain large amounts of synthetic oestrogens, which lead to oestrogen dominance found to be another cause of cancer.

Following further research it became apparent that a large percentage of breast cancers are related to oestrogen, which stimulates the breast cells to divide more rapidly. This increases the risk of the uncontrolled cell growth characteristic of cancer. The more oestrogen a woman is exposed to the greater the risk of breast cancer.

Unopposed oestrogens (without progesterone) that are present in the contraceptive pill have now been conclusively linked with breast cancer. However, there may be enhancement towards protection against cervical cancer.

Oestrogen is produced in significant quantities during the menstrual cycle, which explains why women who start menstrual periods early are at an increased risk. I started at ten years of age, so this applies to me, doesn't it?

Pre-menstrual syndrome, particularly associated with breast tenderness and fluid retention, is also a common feature of oestrogen dominance. Once again, this applied to me.

We were made more aware of consuming cruciferous vegetables, (also known as the brassica family) such as broccoli, cabbage and cauliflower, because they contain a phyto-chemical known as indole-3-carbinol which, in laboratory tests, have shown to inhibit breast cancer cells.

Suzannah Olivier (1999) states "Indole-3-carbinol is of particular interest as, in human studies, it encourages oestrogens to be deactivated, while in animal studies it reduces mammary cancers, is associated with hormonal factors that reduce breast cancer risk, and in one study it prevented breast cancer by a massive 65% and was recommended as a good candidate for chemo-prevention of breast cancer."

There is also evidence that certain pulses and seeds help reduce cancer risks. Lentils and chickpeas are ascribed to substances called isoflavines and lignans that have weak oestrogen-like effects in the body. These have been shown to block the action of the more naturally made oestrogen which helps explain their cancer protective effect.

Healthy fats, known as omega 3 fatty acids, also appear to reduce the risk of breast cancer.

At a later date I was introduced to an unrefined, untreated cold-pressed oil, "Udo's Choice." This provides a rich source of essential fatty acids from a complete vegetarian source.

We were informed that unhealthy diets consumed in the Western world causes 35% of cancer. Dr. Rosy Daniel Healing Foods 1996

Healing Points Dec. 2000 A. Gillanders states "Between 30 and 40 per cent of cancers are directly related to our diets."

As support to this, in one of my own favourite books, 'What's The Alternative' (1995) Hazel Courtney states *"More than a third of all cancer deaths are diet related."*

Mike Hudson, Consultant Surgeon, Queen Elizabeth Hospital, King's Lynn (1999) states *"Diet has been known to be a factor in the development of some cancers for a long time. There are many other factors, of course, but sufficient heed has not been taken of diet, and advice, when given, frequently falls on deaf ears. Eating is a habit after all which, like many other habits, may at first seem hard to change."*

For many years I have said that I believe to a great extent "we are what we eat". Unfortunately today, our environment and lifestyle makes it a lot more difficult to cope with. Vegetables do not contain the nutrients we expect to find in them and because steroids and hormones are administered to enhance animal growth, we are consuming unknown amounts.

Hazel Courtney again *"Is it possible to still eat a healthy balanced diet in today's world? A century ago there were no pesticides sprayed on our crops, nor any of the 3,500 chemical preservatives and additives found in our food today. In country areas the air was cleaner, acid rain did not pollute our crops. There are over 3,000 chemicals in the air, from the lead car exhaust fumes, cadmium from cigarettes to mercury in pesticides. These alone cause hyperactivity, aggressive behaviour, memory loss, confusion and cancer."*

I also looked at The Gerson Therapy. Dr. Max Gerson was a German physician who died in 1959. His therapy is based on optimum nutrition and thorough detoxification. This is achieved by following a strict organic vegetarian diet with huge amounts of fresh raw vegetables and fruit, sometimes liquidised and drastic detoxification with coffee enemas. However, it appeared to be very expensive and a lot of work in the preparation would also be involved. I know that the rest of my family would find it difficult to accept, and I would feel awkward about it. Also, as it initially needs to be followed for two years, at the time of consideration that period of time felt like eternity.

My two sons are in the generation that believe 'burger bars' and 'convenience foods' are the accepted diets in today's society. Although, I hasten to add, that sort of eating is very rare in our household, I am told (by the boys) "we are different" hence I felt the Gerson diet would be rubbing salt into the wound.

The older generation, in my circle of family and friends, still tend to serve traditional meals, consisting of meat, potatoes and two vegetables hence entertaining me eating a Gerson diet could be a little problematic and I don't think it would be fully understood, saying that I would just consume the vegetables

Socialising, by eating out in public houses and restaurants would also be troublesome, because, already it can be difficult to order vegan food from the choice of menus. More places now serve vegetarian foods, yet many of these dishes include dairy products.

On 'weighing up' these different factors, it did not seem to be the right path to follow. However, now I am further down the road, going by my experience and further research I have carried out, if cancer should happen to 'flare up' in me again, I would very seriously consider the Max Gerson regime.

'Cancer' diets in general, appear to be based on Gerson's theory i.e. recommendations of increased intake of fruit and vegetables and reduction of fats. Large amounts of carrot juice is sometimes recommended, which is part of Gerson's therapy. Also, it has been found that porridge, another of Gerson's favourites, also helps regulate blood sugar and fats.

Many books are now available on dietary subjects and I would recommend further reading.

Also, it is mentioned at the beginning of the Bible that we should nourish our bodies with raw fruit and vegetables provided by nature. Could it mean that our bodies are developed for this and we abuse them?

And God said, "Behold, I have provided all kinds of grain and all kinds of fruit for you to eat; but for all the wild animals and for all the birds I have provided grass and leafy plants for food" – and it was done." Genesis 1 29-30

Whilst discussing the importance of diet Prince Charles joined us and took part in the conversation. He was 'very down to earth' agreed with what was being said and explained some of the difficulties he was up against trying to drink two and a half litres of water a day along with his time schedule and travelling. Some of his experience was quite humorous and certainly brought some laughter to all faces in the room, at the time.

Following this discussion, it was time for lunch. Needless to say, a very pleasant healthy buffet was prepared. Many thanks to Jane for the management and all others involved who were able to show off their skills - most impressive. It was also an opportunity to see that in no way was the vegan diet boring or monotonous. Instead, we were able to try novel tastes and flavours.

After lunch, Prince Charles gave a speech to over 100 people, including former patients, supporters, trustees and staff. One of the points he made was that the Centre's message is to look at the 'whole person' when treating cancer, which, he felt was the right approach. He said that he had a strong belief that in order to move forward a more inclusive system needs to be created which incorporates both complementary and conventional medicine. Patients must be given the choice where appropriate and the best of both worlds when possible.

He also hoped that in future years more centres, like Bristol, would develop throughout the country.

Meeting him, and only sitting approximately three feet apart, was a pleasurable experience. On return from Bristol, I decided to write to him explaining how much I supported his Foundation for Integrated Medicine. He returned a letter, signed personally, confirming that he shares similar feelings about the conventional healthcare system.

12th July, 2000

Dear Mrs. Scate

I was immensely touched to receive your letter following our recent meeting at the Bristol Cancer Centre. I am very proud to be so involved with the Centre and never fail to be moved by the examples of courage and fortitude I come across every time I visit.

I share many of your concerns about the conventional healthcare 'system', which denies so much choice to the patient - as you correctly point out. Indeed, since my last visit to Bristol I have made the identical point to a great many people, such is my level of frustration at the slow pace of change in this area. You have my assurance that this is very much on my mind - and that of my Foundation for Integrated Medicine.

This comes with many healing thoughts and my warmest best wishes to you and your family.

Yours most sincerely

Charles

I also spoke to a visiting doctor who had been working with oncology for many years. When I shared my feelings with her that I wanted to stop conventional treatment, she had great understanding and went on to explain that a lot of research had taken place to find that three chemotherapy treatments were as effective as the standard six treatments given for my condition. It would have been be interesting to find the references that supported this.

On mulling this over, I thought it was probably worth the risk of receiving one more treatment, having gone so far already. Maybe this would give some satisfaction that I had given standard treatment a chance as well.

Unfortunately, since this treatment and further research, I have read several articles/books stating facts similar to what Walters R. (1993) wrote in Options The Alternative Cancer Therapy Book "The cancers from which most people die – the big killers like breast, colon and lung cancer – generally do not respond to chemotherapy."

In "A Gentle Way With Cancer" by Brenda Kidman when writing about Dr. Alec Forbes, the first Medical Director appointed at B.C.H.C., she states "'Many of the patients who came into hospital for help had been given medicines which were supposed to be "the treatment" of their disease,' Dr Alec said. 'But what we were seeing was the devastating and sometimes irreversible side-effects of medical treatment aimed at suppressing symptoms rather than dealing with the cause of their diseases."

"The long term effects of chemotherapy can include heart damage, weeks, months or years after treatment; loss of fertility and an increased risk of recurrence of cancer... Most chemo drugs cause secondary cancers. They can appear five, ten, fifteen years after the 'successful' chemotherapy," states Phillip Day

After reading such articles, I realise the importance of continuing my positive outlook, self-motivation and the desire to continue with the nutritional therapies alongside them.

As we all said our farewells, I started to feel uneasy about going home. Even though I had only been there a couple of days, it had provided a great sense of security. Now I felt uneasy about breaking myself away from people who had shown caring and understanding.

In the book "Cancer Why We're Still Dying to Know the Truth" (2000) Phillip Day states "More often than not, cancer victims sense an isolation; realise that something has changed that won't ever be the same again."

This was so true for me at that stage of my life.

However, fellow patients and supporters agreed to exchange addresses, and this gave me reassurance. I looked forward to meeting up again for a residential course sometime later in the year.

Third and final chemotherapy session

Michael and I returned home and I'm pleased to say that some of the energy I sensed at Bristol stayed with me. Following this experience, I felt invigorated and my confidence had been boosted. The professionals had rekindled a fighting spirit.

The next day, I was due to have my third administration of chemotherapy. I attended the oncology clinic. My blood results were satisfactory.

I explained to the doctor that following the seminar, an appointment had been made for a consultation with a doctor in London the next day, hence could I please delay the administration of chemotherapy drugs?

This was not a problem. The doctor understood my feelings and agreed that I was entitled to another opinion.

Friday came and we travelled to London for a consultation with the doctor who had been recommended to us at the seminar.

Neither of us felt particularly impressed with this consultation. She supported chemotherapy treatment and looked upon surgery as a necessity "because the type of cancer I had would only spread anyway" she announced. However, she advised us to seek a second opinion from another oncology consultant in London and advised me to request further investigations with my N.H.S. consultant, which included a blood test for tumour markers (a blood test used to measure the level of a protein material or other chemical produced by cancer cells) and a liver scan.

She then made a further appointment, with me, to administer an intra-venous infusion.

The next day was Michael's birthday. Unfortunately, neither of us felt like celebrating. I felt at very low ebb. Michael did not say much, but knowing him, as I do, I am sure that any form of festivity was very low on his agenda.

He suggested that we should visit a friend, who lived in Woodbridge, the following day, then went on to make the necessary arrangements.

The visit was therapeutic for both of us. It was a very hot day and the sea breeze was welcoming.

On the Monday, I tried to follow the 'usual' pattern – Michael went to work, the boys went to school, I remained dispirited. The words in my diary read: *"I am still at low ebb. What is my purpose in life? I need a goal to aim for, and don't seem to have one at this time. Playing the role of wife and mother at the moment just feels like hard slog with no reward."*

Many people had offered help and support when I first broke the news about my cancer, yet I felt unable to call for help. I felt so listless, anything and everything was an effort. Also, most friends were at work, everybody had duties to carry out.

Poor Michael wasn't well. He had a cold and was languid. To add to his problems, his car would not start! The last thing I felt I could do was to pour more concerns of mine on him. Writing in my diary definitely appeared to have therapeutic properties though.

Trying to contact my consultant's secretary at the hospital added to the frustration.

Three days later my third session of chemotherapy was administered!

Two hours later, the new consultant introduced himself. He appeared very pleasant and concurred with my feelings of using complementary therapies to assist the healing process. He informed me that he was in favour of starting a centre, similar to Bristol, in memory of Helen Rollason, locally and agreed with me joining the team. He also gave consent to the further investigations I requested, which included tumour markers, bone and liver scans.

However following examination of my breast he commented that 86% of breast cancer patients survive routine treatment that I had been prescribed, yet because of my advanced growth my prognosis fell into the smaller category! This really helped confirm that the decision I had made was correct.

Positive feelings were within me because this was definitely going to be my last session of chemotherapy, although, of course, this wasn't mentioned to any of the medical team. I had also managed to drink two litres of water following chemotherapy administration whilst waiting to see the consultant. How much this went towards a decrease in the vomiting that followed I'm not sure because I had also increased the dosage of anti-emetics. Anyway, other side effects such as the metallic taste, apathy and lethargy were still present.

Whilst in bed recovering from the chemotherapy administration, Michael and my father took on the challenge of installing a water fountain in our back garden. This was one of those projects that had only been spoken about before. But now, in considering the therapeutic properties it had to offer, the time seemed right. Hearing the flow of water is so very relaxing. Thanks to you both.

Two Days later

Even though I was feeling rough, obviously life had to go on around me.

Sam, one of James's friends, called to go to the youth club with him. There had been a misunderstanding, and James had already left, so I offered to walk with Sam. I asked if he would like to hold my hand, which he did. His mother spoke to me the next day and said how pleased he was about it and he had even chosen to write about me the next day for his teacher.

Here is a copy. I found it very reassuring to read a nine-year old's opinion, and felt quite touched emotionally.

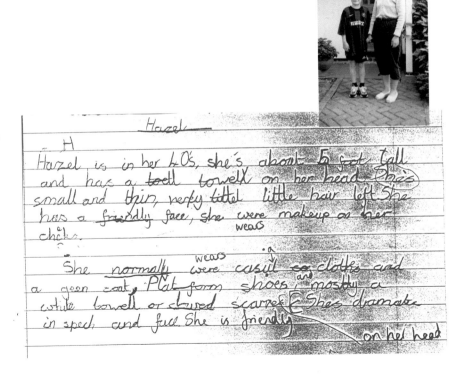

Hazel

H

Hazel is in her 40's, she's about 5 foot tall and has a towell on her head. She's small and thin, very little little hair left. She has a friendly face, she wears makeup on her chiks.

She normally wears casul clothes and a geen coat. Platform shoes and mostly a white towell or chuved scarf. She's dramatic in speech and face. She is friendly on her head

The decision to stop

The following week I returned to London for the infusion therapy and of course, Michael came with me. I approached it with an open mind thinking that perhaps, due to tiredness, unfair judgement had been given about my initial consultation.

However, second time around was even less impressive with the result of feeling shattered on return. I could definitely not continue with this treatment. Any positive effects of the infusion appeared to be undone by the tiredness caused with commuting and the atmosphere in the clinic was not professional, or encouraging.

Four days later, an appointment with a doctor in Kent had been arranged. Michael drove me there.

Dr. Fritz Schellander introduced himself and gave me a thorough consultation, lasting approximately one and a half hours. He listened to my feelings and was very reassuring. He also commented that following examination, the cancer mass did not appear to be as bad as it appeared on the mammogram. If surgery was necessary, he could refer me to somebody privately, whom he felt would show more consideration, because it did not appear that I needed such extensive surgery.

'Good old physical examination'. Why didn't my N.H.S consultant do that?

Following this consultation we felt a lot happier although, initially, Michael was most impressed, because once again tiredness had overtaken me. However, a detailed letter with suggested treatment arrived the next day and following a good night's sleep and time to study the proposed treatment plan we decided to pursue it with a further appointment.

Exactly one week following this consultation Michael's father died. This came as a dreadful shock to the whole family. Dear John had appeared to be perfectly alright in the evening when speaking to Michael's brother on the telephone. Then, less than twenty-four hours later he collapsed, and died at home. My mother-in-law now needed to be cared for because this had been John's role for the past few years.

This meant that Michael would have more responsibilities to carry out. It seemed that making the decision to help myself become more independent had come at just the right time.

We both returned to Kent to discuss my future treatment in more detail with Dr Schellander.

He had qualified as a doctor at Vienna University in 1965 and went on to full-time clinical work and research for several years. He moved to England in 1971 then went on to work as a principal in general practice from 1975 until 1989 before opening his own private practice.

He kept himself informed of the latest international medical thinking and networked with a number of holistic doctors and complementary therapists, increasingly using non-toxic natural therapies. Having completed several years' research into holistic approaches to cancer, he recognised the need for each individual to have a suitable treatment programme.

His approach rests largely on the assumption that cancer is not just a localised disease it is systemic, meaning that a whole system, or collection of systems are involved, hence 'cure' must need more than just localised surgery.

Once again, his strategy was 'in tune' with my feelings. This was to support and enhance the body's defence functions and to mobilize internal healing forces. One of his information leaflets stated "Patients are still able to live with cancer present in their bodies, as long as their defences are kept intact and strong." Fritz's clients are seen as active participants during treatment and are encouraged to learn more about themselves and their illness.

On consultation he just happened to say all the right things. He never poured out sympathy, nor was he condescending or patronising. Instead, he treated me as a 'whole person' and showed instant understanding of my feelings. He encouraged me to pamper myself to get away from routine chores and enjoy complete rest. This is something that I have always found difficult to perform.

However, with Michael's support and encouragement, arrangements were made for me to attend the clinic for three days treatment, which entailed staying away from home for two nights. This would take place just a few days following the consultation.

In the meantime I attended the local oncology clinic and explained my feelings to the doctor about not wanting to continue with conventional treatment. He was very understanding and said the message would be passed on to the consultant. He then informed me that the pathology reports had been received which stated that my breast lump tissue was ER positive (the American abbreviation for oestrogen receptor) hence, Tamoxifen – an oestrogen-modulating drug should be prescribed.

I appreciated that this drug had been tested, with many thousands of women supposedly showing substantial benefits, e.g. a reduction in the recurrence of breast cancer. Tamoxifen is also said to give protection against heart disease and osteoporosis. However, I had inner feelings that I was more likely to fall into the unfortunate group that suffer side effects. I believed that taking Tamoxifen would disrupt things further.

The doctor replied that the clinic had an 'open door' and if ever I should want to return, I would be made welcome. I thanked him for his understanding and parted with a sigh of relief.

Other therapies

I feel sure that the complementary therapies practised on me were very beneficial. Because there is no end of information readily available on these subjects, I will not go into detail about the actual therapies.

The main benefits for me were being able to have somebody who would listen and show some understanding, without being too judgemental, and provide a relaxing, trusting atmosphere.

The release of endorphins, stimulated immune system and circulation also went towards promoting the state of homeostasis. My thanks go out to everybody who played part in this.

Some complementary therapies being practised are potentially very powerful. They should become more recognised and one should be able to incorporate them into an individual's routine healthcare if desired.

There appears to be much confusion, with both practitioners and sufferers, as to whether complementary therapies should be used on people who have cancer. In my experience and research I came across many people who were rather apprehensive about using massage etc. in fear of it 'spreading' the cancer.

Because I found the 'good' outweighed the 'bad', I would like to share some of the positive support with you. One must remember that at the end of the day it is only YOU (the 'patient') who can decide what treatment feels right for you.

Complementary therapies are practised at The Bristol Cancer Help Centre and during my time there, reflexology, reiki, and spiritual healing were all practised on me. Also, in the literature provided, upon leaving the introduction course, there is a list of Professional Practitioner Organisations, 37 in all, that may be contacted for further treatment – aromatherapy, acupuncture massage, reflexology, shiatsu and spiritual healing (therapies that were practised on me) are all included.

"Cancer" is one of "The Natural Way" book series and several therapies are suggested.

Dr. Jeremy Geffen did much research following his father's death from cancer and in his book "The Journey Through Cancer" (2000) several therapies are suggested, massage, aromatherapy, reiki and acupuncture included.

Ann Gillanders in "The Compendium of Healing Points" (2001) says that there is no danger practising reflexology on cancer patients. However, she suggests not using reflexology on one whilst undergoing chemotherapy or radiotherapy, but to wait for a week following treatment. The reason being, that the 'side effects' which may be caused by reflexology detoxifying the body, on top of those caused by chemotherapy and radiotherapy could make the patient feel extremely unwell.

Going by my experience of chemotherapy, the desire for reflexology being practised on me for the first few days following chemotherapy certainly wasn't there! So, once again, we must be guided by the individual's inner feelings.

The Association of Reflexologists held a seminar, in May 2000 entitled Reflexology and Cancer Care and the report written by Freda Magee in the September 2000 Journal states:

"Freda suggested that reflexology can be used as a 'tool' for change i.e. to assist functional biochemical changes in the body, plus psychological and spiritual changes.

The Benefits of Reflexology include:
- Relaxation
- Reduction of tension and anxiety
- Pain/symptom relief
- Improved sleep pattern
- Improved sense of well-being/self esteem/body image
- Time to share feelings/fears

There are two parts to reflexology treatment and they are impossible to separate:

1. The science of reflexology (the doing to)
2. The art of reflexology (the being there for)."

In Healing Points, June 2001, Karen Finch writes an article "Reflexology for Cancer Patients" she had apparently completed a postgraduate course at The Belvior Park Hospital, Belfast (which I meant to do further research on, yet still haven't got 'round to). This article was pointed towards the terminally ill, yet still achieved things like improved sleep and relaxation, which is important to anybody.

Rachel Charles (Mind, Body and Immunity 1990) mentions massage, acupressure and shiatsu among others and can wholeheartedly recommend shiatsu from her own experience.

Valerie Worwood, in her book "The Fragrant Pharmacy" 1990 suggests that if one has breast cancer an aromatherapy massage will be beneficial both pre and post surgery using different formulas to soothe and tone. She also feels that preparing the skin before and after radiation is advantageous and goes on to say that she felt many burns that she has seen in her practice could have been avoided, if aromatherapy had been used. She also states "Treatment with essential oils will not conflict the treatment given by your doctor." Once again, she says that aromatherapy treatment should not be used on the actual day that chemotherapy or radiotherapy is administered, but use it in between and for at least a month following treatment.

In addition, researchers at Memorial Sloan-Kettering Cancer Centre in New York City say that aromatherapy aids cancer treatment.

These were just a few examples of using complementary therapies as part of one's treatment. However, I must stress that they all say that it is only to be 'part' of one's treatment and they all emphasise how important the diet is in preventing the spread of these 'rogue' cells.

In mid-July, I was invited to a barbecue that was being held as a surprise birthday treat for Karen - a colleague with whom I had originally trained to practise reflexology. The weather could have been a lot better, yet we still all had a good time. Numerous people present were familiar, because they were fellow members from The Essex Reflexology Group. This meant they were qualified reflexologists and many practised other therapies as well. I enjoyed the feelings of being in a wonderful restorative atmosphere.

Of course, I must also add that I only consumed 'healthy foodstuff' e.g. the lovely salads that had been prepared to accompany the juicy sausages, burgers etc. that the more healthy people felt able to digest. I am not meaning to show any disrespect and feel sure that vegetarian sausages and burgers were also available. I was more than happy mixing with friends and consuming food that had been prepared for me.

Unfortunately, whilst there, I received a 'phone call saying that my mother-in-law needed medical attention because she had just had a trans-ischaemic attack (T.I.A.) – this was just four days after her dear husband had died.

Oh dear, what could I do? All I can say is that all the therapists surrounding me sent their vibes as if they were electrically charged. The air around me released energies and spirits to go towards my healing and gave me the strength to drive home and face the situation.

I do not mean this to sound "magical" but feel sure that others who have been in similar situations will understand what I mean.

I'm pleased to say that the next day Joyce showed good improvement and continued to progress, enabling her to be present at John's funeral, a few days later.

All I can say is that all went as well as could be expected for an occasion like this. Joyce had made recovery from her T.I.A., the weather was pleasant, John's children had written a lovely address and the service was very fitting. Dear Margaret offered her services and did the catering for us, which was also a great help.

Joyce could not be left by herself, hence, her children (Michael has two sisters and a brother) were taking it in turns to stay with her, whilst at the same time trying to find a suitable residential home for her.

I am pleased to say that a new abode was found for her to settle in approximately six or seven weeks later, where she has been well looked after.

Bristol again

Ten days later, it was time to go to Bristol again. This time it was for a five-day residential course, which was aiming to be a more experiential learning process discovering self-help techniques that could be continued at home.

I felt the main benefits for me would be to enjoy rest and relaxation (which I certainly needed and achieved). I also took advantage of being able to dedicate time towards other people's experience and mine. This all went towards helping me achieve a strong sense of 'self.'

I suppose I was learning that holistic healing was helping to correct life conditions that can predispose cancer 'breaking out.' I was reminded that the mind is immensely powerful and that the relationship between mind and body should never be underestimated. A positive attitude is a major step towards creating a healthy body.

It is a pleasure to say that my positive attitude remained with me throughout my stay at Bristol. I was able to deepen my self-awareness and find new meaning and purpose in life. I enjoyed being able to rise in the morning and go for a walk before returning for gentle exercise followed by breakfast then meditation.

Another pleasant factor was being able to see three other colleagues from the introductory course. We all felt on the same wavelength and were able to compare notes. Unfortunately, one or two of the 'new' people found it difficult to join in to start with. I think this helped make us aware of how important it is to have an introduction, because you either want to adopt the Bristol philosophy or you do not. However, I am pleased to say that harmony developed between us all.

On the fourth evening there, (the penultimate) Pat Pilkington came to speak to us. Pat is a trustee and co-founder of the charity. She is the wife of Rev. Christopher Pilkington and they have always believed that 'healing' was an important part of their pastoral duties.

Over twenty years ago, along with Penny Brohn, she set about changing entrenched medical attitudes towards cancer treatment. Along with patient-power, this change has been brought about and doctors realise that people combining the Bristol Approach with medical treatment can achieve positive results.

She asked us to close our eyes and practise meditation. Unfortunately, for me, during this time I 'nodded off!' However, I remember Pat saying that if we would like to send her a photograph of oneself she would put it in the chapel and we would be remembered in her daily prayer.

When I arrived home, I asked Thomas to do the honours of taking a photograph for me, because the sun was still shining and it felt pleasant in our back garden.

It was also whilst in Bristol that I plucked up the courage to take my scarf/hat off. It was lovely to 'feel free'. I was always so conscious of my headgear – what did it look like? Was it straight or falling off? Then, whilst sitting, and trying to rest my head, the knot would very often be in an uncomfortable position.

Now I was comfortable. I am sorry if others didn't like my appearance, but there wasn't much I could do about it. I had asked other people's opinion, in Bristol, before removing it, yet nobody had objected.

I shall always remember the last evening there celebrating the week. Kitchen staff, once again, showed off their skills by preparing 'healthy' nibbles and punch to drink.

Lovely music was played and we were taught different movements to practise to the rhythms.

I commented on how much I particularly liked one piece of music. Andrew informed me that it was "The Entrance of The Queen of Sheba" taken from Pachelbel. We joined together in a circle and were taught simple steps to perform to this rhythm.

Six months later, Andrew wrote to tell me that he had married. A couple of days later, I went shopping to purchase a card for him. After buying a suitable card, I visited the health shop. What music should happen to be playing in the background? Yes, that's right –'Entrance of the Queen of Sheba.'

Needless to say, I had to purchase this cassette. It is 'special' to me. It is often played – sometimes I will just lay back and relax with it playing softly in the background. On other occasions, it may be playing whilst doing household chores, e.g. ironing. I also try to practise the steps we were taught. This might sound crazy to you, yet to me it is very therapeutic.

Kent treatment starts

A couple of days later I returned to Kent. I decided I wanted to drive myself there, as a further step towards my independence, instead of being taken and collected as originally planned. Besides, I felt dear Michael certainly had enough to do now – helping with the caring of his mother as well as funeral arrangements. He did not even have time to mourn, poor soul.

I felt pleased with myself arriving at the clinic independently. All the staff made me feel very welcome. This was certainly a step in the right direction to boost my healing properties, because treatment for cancer should be physical, mental, emotional and spiritual. Having had this experience, I feel that there is definitely a strong link between emotions and physical well-being.

A good framework of honesty, realism and mutual co-operation was established and I felt that my cancer could now be viewed as 'more curable.' This was not meant to oversimplify the problem – I appreciate that taking that attitude could be just as fatal as believing that no treatment could be given.

Blood tests were taken and Fritz informed me that one of the tumour marker readings was slightly elevated and he 'would keep an eye on this.' However, I am pleased to add that following my chosen treatment path these figures went down, indicating that the cancer has been eliminated. Fritz suggested that this test should be repeated occasionally because if the level should happen to rise again it is an early indication that the cancer has either recurred in that area, spread to nearby lymph glands or metastasised to another organ.

Local hyperthermia was chosen and the plan was to receive this on a daily basis whilst at the clinic. Hyperthermia is made up from the Greek words hyper - to raise and therme - to heat.

A statement from a medical paper by Dr. T. K. Hei, et al, of the college of Physicians, Columbia University (April 2 1986) states: *"Hyperthermia is the only agent to treat cancer that does not itself appear to be oncogenic (i.e. cancer-inducing)....In contrast, most chemotherapeutic agents used clinically at present, are carcinogenic in their own right."*

Because the vascular system to tumour cells is restricted, they tend to become tightly packed and congested. The blood flow in the tumour area becomes extremely sluggish, so under high heat, temperatures continue to rise to destructive levels.

The rationale behind me receiving this treatment was because cancer cells are more heat-sensitive than normal cells, they would be broken down under excessive heat.

A wealth of rapidly accumulating evidence indicates that even a local application of hyperthermia stimulates and enhances the body's natural immune mechanism as a whole. It is a non-invasive treatment utilizing technology to generate heat to specific areas of the body where cancer is located.

I was made comfortable on a couch. The tumour was heated to a temperature between 107 and 113 degrees Fahrenheit, using highly focused radio-frequency waves. These break down the tumour mass without harming the surrounding healthy tissue. Treatment was controlled with sensors and computer-guided applicators.

This method of treatment has been approved by the United States Food and Drug Administration as a medical procedure for treating cancer. However, many patients have not heard about it, even though in the U.S.A. it is currently used on approximately ten thousand patients per year. It is also accepted as standard therapy in other countries, such as Japan, China, Germany and Italy.

Why aren't more people able to benefit from it?

As far as I know, it is only used in England, at one of the London Hospitals, for patients who have secondary cancer and already undergone radiation.

If hyperthermia became widespread, would there be some loss in the huge profits made by the supporters of chemotherapy and radiation? Perhaps this helps explain the medical establishment's continual resistance.

Whilst in the clinic I also had intravenous infusions administered. The main purpose being to expose my body to concentrated dosages of nutrients and to prevent any inactivation that could be caused by digestion. Another exciting concept was the fact that these are non-toxic – completely opposite to the chemicals administered this way during chemotherapy treatment. Within weeks of my initial intravenous treatment I began to feel stronger and felt as though I was 'blossoming'. Fatigue began to lift and I felt reborn.

Some of the nutritional supplements administered this way included:

Laetrile (Vitamin B17) / Amygdalin

This substance is highly concentrated in the pits of apricots and was used by Chinese doctors for the treatment of tumours, some 3,500 years ago. It was first identified as an anticancer agent by a noted biochemist Ernest Krebs, Jr., Ph D. as stated under "botanicals as cancer medicines" in "An Alternative Medicine Definitive Guide to Cancer" (1997)

Many studies show evidence of laetrile / amygdalin efficacy.

At the C.A.I.B. seminar, Ralph Moss informed us of that he was 'fired' from an American Hospital because he revealed an apparent cover-up by authorities regarding positive findings about laetrile. He informed us that research findings were suppressed, as it was against the interests of the pharmaceutical industry, presumably because the substance is non-patentable.

Laetrile is a natural, low cyanide-containing substance and is found in the seeds of apricots, apples, cherries, plums and peaches. It is also present in buckwheat, millet, strong watercress and cassava melons.

When I mentioned taking 'B17'/Laetrile as a form of treatment, I sometimes had the response from others that *'Laetrile contains cyanide, so I wouldn't take that.'* Three excellent books to gain insight into the positive effects of vitamin B17 on cancer is *'Cancer: Why We're Still Dying to Know the Truth,'* and *'B17 Metabolic Therapy'* by Phillip Day. Also, *'The Even Better Good News About Cancer'* by Richards and Hourigan.

In theory, B17/Laetrile appears to be the perfect selective 'search and destroy' substance for cancer therapy. As always, one must make sure that the treatment comes from a reliable source, because poor quality control and incorrect packing can make the material quite useless.

Some therapists believe that laetrile can ease the pain of secondary cancers, control nausea and help tumour shrinkage. Some suggest up to five kernels three times a day on an empty stomach, leaving four hours between doses. Other recommendations say up to 40 kernels a day during the acute stage.

There are no known side effects, some people say that they should be eaten with a vegetarian diet, others do not support this. Many biscuits also contain laetrile in smaller quantities.

As far as I am aware, no conclusive research has established that this natural therapy causes any harm at all – there are no recordings of a victim of this therapy. Unfortunately, the same cannot be said for some people who have undergone painful and often ineffectual surgery, radiation and chemotherapy.

Richards & Hourigan states "Amygdalin, widely and best known as Laetrile, is the most abused, misused and misunderstood remedy in the history of cancer treatment. It is our opinion that it combines a powerful and rapidly cancericidal action with a toxicity that is so slight as to be negligible. It has been hailed as a wonder drug in some quarters; this is something of an exaggeration. It has been condemned as a worthless quack remedy by others either because they are genuinely misinformed or because they were **barefaced and deliberate liars.** Outside of our own albeit considerable personal experience we, the authors, have had considerable difficulty in eliciting hard, factual/unprejudiced information on this subject."

Hydrogen Peroxide was also administered to me intravenously. This is made by normal healthy human body cells to help regulate metabolism, also to act as a poison in the process of destroying invaders.

Many experiments have been carried out with intravenous hydrogen peroxide being used as treatment for heart and chest conditions, arthritis, candida, and chronic fatigue syndrome, all with excellent results. Research has also shown that hydrogen peroxide provides an additional boost to the anti-cancer defences. This is achieved by stimulating natural killer cells, which are needed to stop the spreading of cancer cells.

When given at the correct dosage, it can help regulate tissue repair, growth, immune and energy functions and the hormonal system.

An Alternative Medicine Definitive Guide to Cancer (1997) supports this theory by stating "According to Dr Farr, oxidation achieved through H_2O_2 therapy regulates tissue repair, cellular respiration, growth, immune and energy functions, most hormone systems, and the production of cytokines (chemical messengers that are involved in the regulation of almost every system in the body)."

Other benefits are a heightened sense of well-being, including increased mental clarity and energy levels. These responses could be related to the release of pure oxygen, thereby saturating all the body cells and tissues with this life-giving element.

D.H.E.A. mentioned earlier, was also prescribed by Dr. Schellander. This hormone protects the body against the ravages of out-of-control stress hormones. As stress levels rise, D.H.E.A. declines. Research has shown that when levels of D.H.E.A. decline in our bodies, we can suffer the damaging effects of stress hormones.

Experiments show that D.H.E.A. has anti-cancer properties. In the book *"The Super Hormone Promise"* (1997) William Regelson and Carol Colman state *"Dr. Schwartz told us about a British cancer researcher who had found that the D.H.E.A. levels were abnormally low in women with breast cancer. No one knows why."*

Later in the same book, it reads, "D.H.E.A. appears to protect against a wide range of carcinogens and many different forms of cancer. For example, D.H.E.A. supplementation in their food prevented breast cancer in a strain of female mice that are prone to die from it." This supports the research mentioned earlier in 'The Seminar' section. It, therefore, certainly seemed worthwhile to take one small tablet on a daily basis.

Melatonin was another recommendation. This hormone is produced in the pineal gland and regulates the body's sleep/wake cycle. Peak production occurs at night while we are sleeping and blood levels are ten times what they are during the day when melatonin levels off.

Apparently, when our body clocks strike 'middle age' in our forties melatonin levels drop sharply and the pineal gland also tends to shrink. Production of melatonin then becomes erratic and nightime peaks are not as high as they once were. This decline alerts other glands of the body to wind down. In women, the ovaries stop functioning and the menopause begins. The immune system also begins to decline making us more vulnerable to disease such as cancer. (This is told in more detail in The Super Hormone Promise 1996)

One of the reasons for cancer being rare in children and young adults is because their immune systems are functioning optimally by rooting out abnormal cells before they do any damage. Several studies have shown that melatonin can thwart the growth of breast cancer cells in both test tube cultures and living, breathing animals.

The odds of a woman getting breast cancer increase exponentially as melatonin levels decline with ageing. However, by restoring the melatonin levels we can recover the 'youthful advantage' that helped keep these diseases at bay when we were 'in our prime.' (See Melatonin as a

Cancer Treatment in "The Super Hormone Promise.")

After doing a little research it would appear that melatonin helps restore balance to our bodies by helping regulate other hormones. Because my aim is to restore normalcy, I accepted Fritz's advice and started taking melatonin before retiring at night.

My stay at the clinic was very therapeutic. I was warmly welcomed into a lovely atmosphere. Receptionists and other therapists, who work in the clinic were all warm and friendly. On repeat visits, I almost felt like one of the family. Some rapport also developed with other patients who attended for different forms of treatment on a regular basis.

When receiving treatment, I was accommodated in an adjacent ground floor flat, which is within walking distance of shops and restaurants, hence during my stay I was able to rest, relax, exercise, eat and drink sensibly and sleep well which were all contributory factors towards my healing process.

After returning from my first stay in Kent, the three other members of my family passed positive comments on my appearance – these were all said at various times in different parts of the household, hence the fact that one hadn't been stimulated by another. This helped boost my confidence that the pampering and extra treatments were worthwhile.

Before leaving the clinic, I had booked myself in for repeat treatments lasting three days three weeks later and continued to do this for nearly five months, after which great improvement had been made. I had felt back to my 'old self' for the latter part of this time and felt elated when the consultant suggested I left it for three months before returning, after which a six-month break could be considered.

During this time, Christine had called in to see me to see how I was progressing. Of course I had explained to her that I was putting a 'hold' on the conventional treatment.

As she was leaving, she informed me that she had abnormal cervical smear results. Although we all had fingers and toes crossed, unfortunately, this proved to be cancer of the uterus. (The risk of this occurring had been increased by taking hormone antagonists).

Once again, Christine appeared to accept it very well, by keeping up her positive approach. She had already made holiday arrangements for a week away with her husband and agreed to have further chemotherapy administered when she returned.

Looking back over my lifestyle

At the time of diagnosis and being told that my cancer was advanced I responded with the question "How long has it been there?" The consultant found this difficult to answer yet felt that it had been there at least a couple of years.

Looking back over my lifestyle, things had changed a fair amount over the previous two years. The main factors were that Michael and I had to make big changes in our career paths within a few months of each other, which brought about changes in our lifestyle.

As mentioned in the introduction, the hospital at which I was working had to be closed. Because the position offered to me in the new site would entail working irregular hours, including day and night time shifts, it would have been difficult to continue practising complementary therapies. Many clients were used to making appointments weeks in advance yet I wouldn't always be aware of the shift hours I would be working. Whilst at the local hospital I followed the same rota on a fortnightly basis, hence this had never been a problem. On 'weighing it up', I achieved a lot more satisfaction practising complementary therapies because I was able to build a rapport with clients and achieve satisfaction which had diminished a lot in my nursing role. Some of this was due to the quick patient turnover. Also, with my part-time hours, I didn't have much chance to get to know patients as individuals.

Michael's career in the bank had also come to a halt just a couple of months prior to this.

These alterations had made quite a change in the household and in some ways had made it difficult for the children to adapt, particularly Thomas, who was also going through adolescent changes at the time.

Although I was not aware of feeling stressed, because I still socialised and enjoyed different forms of relaxation, there were changes in my body that I was unaware of. Generally, stress has some influence on the electromagnetic fields that surround all living cells and these becoming disrupted had an influence on my immune system. Being conscious of having a lot more indigestion I related this to a small hiatus hernia that's present. Since being diagnosed with cancer I feel that part of the cause may have been emotions affecting my solar plexus plus related digestive organs, resulting in indigestion. Although a healthy diet was consumed the goodness was not properly absorbed, hence a weakened immune system making me more susceptible to illness.

I put other feelings of imbalance down to 'menopausal changes' as I feel sure that many other women of my age do. Let us learn from my experience that we must always stop and listen. Life is a learning process and going out of balance and illness occurring is intended to help us understand ourselves better. Health will come when we regain harmony, leaving the body to begin its own natural process. Emotional equilibrium also needs to be maintained then the mind and body will remain in a state of health.

Many books have been written about healing oneself. This will be part of medicine in the future and I was pleased to find that on consultation with my G.P., when first diagnosed, he independently told me to think positive as it would play a large part in my future recovery. I originally never thought that this would be his belief.

It is definitely the way forward, or are we going round in a circle because Hippocrates pointed out over 2,000 years ago that we have unbelievably powerful health capability within us that wards off disease!

However, psychoneuroimmunology has now been able to prove that the nervous and immune systems have the power to respond to each other via secretion and reception of certain chemicals. This discovery is very important because it has now proven that inner thoughts are able to influence how the lymphocytes (white blood cells) behave i.e. 'mind over matter.'

The cause of my cancer isn't obvious to me. I sometimes wonder if I have some predisposition genetically. Both my parents, now in their seventies, have lived a healthy life with no illness. My father's parents lived 'til their late eighties, although his mother had undergone a mastectomy, because of cancer, over twenty years prior from which she made full recovery. (Chemotherapy was not available as routine treatment in those days.) I never met my grandfather on my mother's side because he died suddenly at the age of fifty-six and her mother lived a full life until the age of eighty-six when she quietly passed away.

However, two of my mothers' sisters and one brother died of

cancer, all in their fifties and one other sister has pulled through both uterine and breast cancer (about twenty years apart). On my father's side of the family, one brother, one half-brother and one half-sister passed away because of cancer. Hence, there may be something genetic lingering in me.

There are many other predisposing factors, including smoking, poor diet, excessive alcohol, the contraceptive pill, H.R.T., working with asbestos, radiation and some chemicals, some viruses, none of which apply to me. You may remember reading earlier, that at the C.A.I.B. seminar it was claimed that four agents have to be present to cause mutation, which results in malignancy.

I will never know what my factors were, (although I also appreciate that 'stress' may have played some part) yet being made more aware of them has enabled me to review my lifestyle from a different angle and I believe that this awareness will enhance my immune system and help safeguard me against my cancer cells taking over.

My Experience of saying 'No' to a Consultant

As previously mentioned, the doctor who saw me at the time I decided to take a break from the conventional route in hospital was very understanding towards my feelings. However, out of politeness, I wrote to the senior consultant and explained the situation myself and he responded by asking me to attend the clinic again.

Once again, Michael and I had to sit in the waiting room for about an hour and a half before being called into the clinic and asked to remove the appropriate clothing. The doctor who had been pleasant and understanding at the previous appointment then appeared – much to our surprise. I explained that a letter had been received from the consultant, asking me to attend.

Following an apology, I was asked to get dressed again, in order to move to another room. I found this very tiring, when it could have so easily been avoided with better management.

Unfortunately, the consultation was not a pleasant experience at all. The consultant made eye contact, with me, then went on to say that if I didn't follow the treatment regime being offered I would soon die. Obviously, this was rather distressing - a picture of his face making eye contact with me often reflects in my memory!

Michael, being the onlooker, also found it extremely upsetting, particularly on finding the consultant so dismissive of the letter he had received from Dr. F. Schellander outlining the less-invasive treatment regime that was to be practised on me.

It was so hard to believe that on a prior consultation, when he took it for granted that I would follow the conventional treatment right through, he was so much in favour of complementary therapies. Now, he would not consider trying to learn more from another doctor's research and experience.

Following this Michael accepted the offer from a fellow therapist for some treatment, which helped him overcome the experience and get back into balance.

Tolerating disagreement is bad enough but words like this could be very destructive. They could have had enormous impact and many people would have 'given up.' Having worked in clinics before, as a nurse, I had some awareness of similar instances, resulting in me talking to the patient, following consultation, with the aim of renewing self-esteem.

I was able to accept the consultant's manner, went home, had a good cry and took myself to bed for a much-needed sleep. (This day, August 17th 2000, was also Thomas's fifteenth birthday, poor soul).

Bernie Siegel(1986) states in his book Love, Medicine and Miracles "I wish both doctors and patients would read 'Edwards' Credo' – doctors so they'll stop undoing the potential benefits of their medicines with the destructiveness of their words, and patients so they'll be inspired to defy those doctors who persist in sentencing their patient to death."

I was aware that cancer being present in my body could mean that death may have occurred; yet, I did not want to increase the risk by introducing violent pathogens. I still could not see the purpose of having chemotherapy - my whole body did not need treatment in that way. Yes, I needed nurturing, yet, as far as I knew, it was only my right breast that had cancer. My chest X-ray and liver scan showed no cause for concern. I was still awaiting a bone scan and must admit that having had back problems for many years there was a glimmer of concern in my own mind that something may 'show up' on this. However, I'm pleased to say that it showed the 'all clear.'

The consultant found it difficult to accept my thoughts. There was not a 'two-way partnership' (as originally thought) which I feel is needed for healing to take place. He said that he would make arrangements for me to see a counsellor and a breast care nurse and also mentioned a date for me to return to his clinic.

The weeks passed by and nobody contacted me, as promised. Whilst visiting my G.P., routinely, I informed him of the situation yet also told him that I wasn't unduly concerned. However, soon afterwards an appointment for the clinic arrived. The date was inconvenient for me and because, by this time, I had noticed improvement in my condition I decided to write back to inform them that at this stage of my illness I did not want to return to the clinic.

My feelings were supported by further research, including

Josef Issels (1999) states in *Cancer. A Second Opinion* "The malignant, crab-like cellular malfunction, which began to multiply at bewildering speed in their body tissue, will for those countless millions, tragically bring the realisation that their cancer could not be cured, controlled or even contained, by the usual methods of surgery, radiotherapy and chemotherapy. Four out of every five persons who receive one, or all, of these treatments die within five years. That is not only an indication of the destructive power of the disease, but also a sobering reflection on the limits of standard techniques, and the concepts of cancer on which they are based."

As support to my fears of not wanting surgery performed: Sir John Bruce, Professor of Clinical Surgery at Edinburgh University, Scotland, said it should not be assumed that he, or any other surgeon, was satisfied with the contribution surgery had made to managing cancer, that "the future lies elsewhere than in the operating room."

As far back as 1938 other surgeons have made similar statements.

It must never be forgotten that any form of surgery/anaesthetic constitutes certain risk factors.

Issels J. (1999) states "It needs boldness, courage and an honest recognition that a grave mistake has been made before escape is possible. The medical profession must show the way."

Because thought precedes everything and is a very powerful medium for transferring energy, positive thoughts were needed please – optimism, friendship, hope and encouragement. Please leave negative thoughts and pessimism behind.

I believe that cancer, like many other major illnesses, cannot be stopped by only using medical treatment, yet would still have liked to work together as a team. Couldn't we still learn from one another?

When the consultant was asked, "what is the success rate and what are the side effects of the treatment you are offering" he said there were positive statistics yet when asked for a copy of these figures to take home and study he was unable to provide it.

It is crucial that patients should have a better understanding of medical terms. For instance, a response (also called a remission) is the definition given if a tumour shrinks by 50% for at least one month. I feel sure that patients in general are not conscious of this. Everybody should also be aware that when doctors describe a treatment as having an excellent response rate, this might not correlate with an increase in overall patient longevity. The quality of life also needs to be considered. Some conventional treatments may provide significant benefits such as pain relief, yet others are highly toxic and make patients so sick that it is said 'the treatment is worse than the disease.' *(I fell into this category)*

As stated before all cancer drugs are toxic at the applied dosages and markedly immunosuppressive, destroying one's natural resistance to many diseases including cancer. The primary effect is poisonous. Because these poisons cannot distinguish between cancerous and normal cells, they disrupt or kill normal healthy cells throughout the body besides attacking the tumour. The bone marrow is attacked, thereby destroying the white cells, which would normally fight infection; the red cells, which are responsible for carrying life-sustaining oxygen to the body's organs; and the platelets, which are responsible for blood clotting. Unfortunately, these immune-system cells are a major part of the body's built in defence system that is needed to fight against cancer.

"How can healing take part if so many 'good' cells are destroyed?" I ask myself.

As further support to my inner feelings I later read Plague, Pestilence and the Pursuit of Power by Steven Ransom (2001) and in the appendix it states ".....as a chemist trained to interpret data, it is incomprehensible to me that physicians can ignore the clear evidence that chemotherapy does much much more harm than good." – Alan C. Nixon, PhD, former president of the American Chemical Society

Life goes on

As I said earlier, it was Thomas's birthday. He was fifteen years old and we did our best to celebrate. I was feeling quite well within myself by this time. We took Thomas out for a meal, at a restaurant of his choice. His aims were to train as a chef and whilst eating he said that one day he would own a restaurant, which he would furnish in the same way as the one he had chosen to dine in.

A week later, it was time to take James to a holiday camp in Norfolk. Sam would also be there. It was originally arranged because Sam's Mum would be working, and going along the original route of treatment, we thought I would be reasonably bed-bound by now!

Anyway, as mentioned earlier I was now able to take James to Norfolk, instead of relying on Sam's parents. It was a pleasant day, Michael and I drove him there and bid farewell for a few days.

It was time to collect him again on Saturday. We asked Thomas if he would like to join us, because we intended driving over to Wells–Next–The –Sea after collecting James. This, being an area where we had enjoyed family holidays in the past.

Thomas didn't find it appealing and chose to stay at home.

Late that afternoon he contacted me on my mobile 'phone and asked if I would soon be home, because he was offering to prepare some tea for us. I explained that we were on our way to Thetford Forest where we were planning to have a picnic tea and 'explore' the woodland with the aim of arriving home about 9p.m.

All went according to plan and I can say, from my heart, that I had a very enjoyable day. I had been physically active and able.

Thoughts went through my mind that if I had gone along the original path of orthodox treatment it would not have been possible to take part like this. In fact, it would probably have meant that Sam's parents would kindly have collected James for me, in order for me to reserve my energy.

Anyway, who knows? All I can say is that I really appreciated being able to do it.

We eventually arrived home about 8.45p.m. Thomas was out.

When I walked into the kitchen look what was waiting for me-

WHAT A SURPRISE!

This really was "icing on the cake." I could not wait for him to get back and have a big hug. I am pleased to say that I did not have too long to wait.

September 2000 Aqua Treatment

One of the people to come forward and offer me complementary treatment was Pat Morrell, who developed Morrell Reflexology approximately twenty years ago, and is now recognised worldwide.

Since then, she has also introduced 'aqua touch'. This involves the person to be treated being eased into the water and supported, by practitioners, who then carry out the delicate, subtle movements of the therapy.

Whilst practising on me one day, she informed me that a small party of therapists and patients were going to The Optimum Energy Clinic, in Guernsey, (see Appendix 2) where she had been asked to open a 'dolphin pool' (the name given to a small treatment pool) and would I like to join them?

Pat had practised aqua treatment on me once already and I was keen to join the party providing I could get a flight.

This I was able to do and going to Guernsey was another lovely, fulfilling experience.

George, who is the owner of the clinic, was very welcoming and made our stay very pleasurable. He is a member of the British Register of Complementary Practitioners, has trained in both Morrell Reflexology and Aqua Touch, which he practises, amongst other therapies.

As mentioned earlier, Pat was asked to officially open the new dolphin pool, that George had had added to his clinic. Guess who was asked to be the patient? Yes that's right, it was me!

I felt quite honoured and it was an experience that neither myself, nor the practitioners, will ever forget. The amount of energy around me was immeasurable, both onlookers and therapists could see thousands of tiny bubbles, being made, in the water around me, and I could feel them. Practitioners tell me that they had never seen one like it before, or since.

Water therapy, itself, is very beneficial to cancer patients anyway. I have read different articles that state it is very therapeutic, can stimulate the immune system, increase the white cell count and aid the body in purging itself of accumulated toxins. Along with that and producing a state of general relaxation, it must aid towards the healing process, mustn't it?

It was a lovely break. I had plenty of rest and spoke to many interesting people.

George, himself, had also experienced cancer, therefore had good understanding of my situation. He said that in order to succeed one needs positive thought, determination and follow a good diet.

There we are – another good living example.

Seven months have passed
"Knowledge is Power"

Seven months after my diagnosis I am pleased to say that I felt 'back to normal'. It was the middle of November and Michael and I agreed that it would be nice to go away on holiday. To fit in with school holidays this would mean going away over the Christmas / New Year period. We both found this to be rather appealing and I am pleased to say that we managed to book a holiday in The Caribbean.

The rest was very therapeutic for me. I really did see wonderful waves rolling on to sandy beaches and palm trees to rest under, as I had previously visualised. I felt that it brought a nice close to the year 2000 and a lovely fresh start to 2001.

This photograph was taken before leaving for the holiday - the year 2000 was over in the house. We would not be returning 'til the year 2001.

Michael & Thomas asked me to include this photograph somewhere in the book, because it was the only photograph taken of 'The Scade Family' together during the year 2000.

On January 17th 2001, it was exactly nine months since my day of diagnosis, and I had made an appointment with my G.P. He pleasantly greeted me and informed me that he was pleased with the blood results that had been received.

I then explained my reasons for still not wanting to receive conventional treatment. The main ones being because I so much enjoyed massaging clients and giving other different forms of complementary treatment, a break of two to three months to have surgery performed, was totally unappealing. I was also concerned that lymphatic swelling could be a complication afterwards, which would deter me from this form of work and that would mean a large chunk of my life would have been taken from me – NOT just my breast.

"If I contracted cancer, I would never go to a standard cancer treatment centre. Cancer victims who live far from such centres have a chance." Professor Charles Mathe, French cancer specialist, stated by Ransom S. (2001) supported what I was saying.

Another factor that didn't help was poor Christine now in bed all the while. Her pain was being controlled with morphine. When I called in to see her we could normally manage to have a few smiles and maybe a few words, yet I couldn't get away from the fact that her time in this world was limited and she was never going to be able to 'walk' again.

I also made my G. P. aware of this.

My dear doctor could see my point of view and supported me 100%. He showed his appreciation of the fact that I had done adequate research into finding this less invasive path that I was following and appeared to understand my feelings. There is no doubt, in my mind, that his reaction is another positive fact towards reaching my goal.

A New Year policy I made was not to overwork myself (yet I must say that I hadn't felt overworked before). This year I decided not to see clients on Wednesdays, this would be classed as 'my day'. The idea being that if I had been busy for two days I could then enjoy complete rest before working for another two days.

Hastening to add that I enjoy my work, I must also say that this policy appears to have been beneficial. I think it makes me feel quite 'special' – at last I am considering myself rather than always giving others priority as I felt may have been the situation before.

Prior to my diagnosis, I generally felt tired all the while and had accepted this was part of our modern lifestyle – generally struggling to do more in less time and also thought it had to be accepted as part of a menopausal change in my body.

However, I now realise that this was a warning sign that my body was out of balance and I would really like to stress to others how important it is to 'listen' to your inner self.

Over the years the woman's role has generally changed and after accomplishing great strides in different career paths more women are following full time work plans whilst still responsible for many chores that are required for running a home.

I feel the importance of making these people more aware of their own body's needs. A break needs to be taken in order to look at oneself. Maybe a rest is needed, or is a healthy snack needed in order to replenish oneself? Is a brisk walk called for?

I feel that, in general, not enough exercise or fresh air is taken in. Not only is it invigorating to enjoy fresh smells of nature and get some sunshine, research has shown that cancer patients who spend two hours or more outdoors each day have greater longevity compared to cancer patients who stay indoors. I appreciate that this goal would be difficult for many to achieve, yet still a little is better than nothing. Also, studies have shown that regular, consistent movement at least three times a week for thirty minutes adds twenty-five per cent more energy to every waking moment.

Many cancer patients may have trouble reaching this goal to start with, yet they can gradually work up to it. However, one must not overwork oneself because excessive exercise can actually cause toxicity through the creation of free radicals, hence overexertion is not recommended.

Because I believe that illness is created by an imbalance of energy, instead of just looking at my breast, I considered my whole self in order to achieve my desired goal.

Thinking of my body as a city constructed of many streets, roads and alleys I tried to find the right route for me. I also appreciate that many other routes could have been taken by only thinking of the times that I have been in London following my A-Z maps. Although I may have started and finished at the same points, different routes have been taken. It is therefore up to each individual to decide which route they want to pursue.

Doctors, consultants and practitioners will give advice yet cannot do the work for us. The patient must seek the source of the problem. All elements of life-style need to be considered e.g. food, exercise, career, relaxation and sleep when making an assessment to achieve better health.

It is an ongoing process and one must not 'give up' – we need to maintain our body's equilibrium and not go out of balance. Learning to listen to our own body language is very important and one should trust their own instincts, whether orthodox, complementary or both. There is no right or wrong.

Changes often need to be made.

This experience has been quite an ordeal yet it has enabled me to discover my own capabilities. By raising my awareness that I should no longer take my body for granted, I have learned to say 'no' and not overwork myself. Instead of ignoring 'tiredness' as I did before, I try to make time for a rest/visualisation. I have also changed my work plan and have put time aside for myself to do what I want to do. This could be carrying out an outstanding chore, the completion of which gives satisfaction, socialising with a friend, or just sitting down and reading a good book for a change.

Fighting to survive has taken much effort and I must admit that at times it has felt rather an ordeal! However, because of having an enquiring awareness, a better life-style has become apparent. The door to bad health has been closed whilst another door appears to have opened to let in light and vitality! It has increased my inner strength and being able to write this book and share my experience with others has been very fulfilling.

As is said in the bible it is up to us to take up thy bed and walk!

With all this in mind, I thought it would be useful to briefly go over the sort of lifestyle I try to lead now.

Summary of my own experience

I have developed positive thoughts with rigid determination, remembering that we are all human beings and come across certain setbacks. Learning to recognise them for what they are is important, any necessary corrections can then be made. If I come across these hiccoughs I have learned to re-focus and start again with renewed zest.

A balance has been restored in my lifestyle, which, I believe has gone a long way towards coping and recovery.

When I first started along this path I found some clauses written by Louise Hay were very helpful. These are:

Today.......I open a new door to self-esteem and self worth.

Today......I lovingly accept my decisions, knowing I am always free to change.

(Sorry, but I cannot remember which book these were in).

I have managed to put more time aside for myself, during which time I can relax, visualise or meditate. It has also become apparent that just ten minutes might be enough, whereas before I always thought that to have a rest one must have an hour of spare time. Sometimes, just taking a few deep breaths may be enough to bring about relaxation, by making me aware of present circumstances and adapt to coping with them.

I can practise visualisation very easily now. Instead of tension developing whilst waiting in a queue, visualisation is practised and this brings a great feeling of warmth and satisfaction.

Now knowing the need to attain peak immunity I am more conscientious of what I consume. Satisfaction is achieved, following a meal that I know has nourished and done me some good. The main problem has been to satisfy other people at the same time.

Fortunately, many of my friends think along the same line, hence eating/drinking with them has not been too hard to deal with.

My two sons have found it difficult, sometimes, because I am told that most of their colleagues eat diets consisting of a high percentage of convenience foods including white bread, fizzy drinks and sweets. I have done my best to explain the importance of following this regime and have tried to meet 'half-way' occasionally serving different meals – particularly the desserts! I appreciate how difficult it is for them, with all the media around and, as far as we can see, all their friends appear to be enjoying good health.

I am able to remember the days when Mum would take me to buy fresh seasonal vegetables on a daily basis, instead of relying on manufactured convenience foods, as many working families do today. The younger generation still need to learn more about the principles of nutrition in order to improve health and provide a good insurance policy against chronic health problems in their future years.

However, I have the satisfaction of knowing what a positive difference the consumption of 'healthy' diets has made to many people that I have met during my profession. It is also encouraging to know that many people who have followed anti-cancer diets similar to the 'Bristol' diet have found that symptoms from other illnesses e.g. diabetes, arthritis have also disappeared.

Before being diagnosed with cancer I became aware of how balancing blood sugar levels helps improve mood swings. There have been many books and magazine articles written to support this in the fields of pre-menstrual syndrome.

The surge of insulin levels is the main factor behind this problem and it has been recorded that women with high insulin levels have a greater risk of breast cancer. I make sure that, generally, three nutritious meals are eaten each day, sometimes healthy snacks are consumed in between. Protein is included in every meal because this reduces surges in insulin levels.

Organic food should be consumed whenever it is possible because pesticides mimic oestrogen in the body and cause the same reactions to occur.

Because numerous research studies have found low levels of certain nutrients are associated with breast cancer I decided to take extra supplements as well as consuming a variety of foods.
These include:

- **Betacarotene** – converts to Vitamin A yet has additional protective factors not found in Vitamin A. Almost every study of cancer and nutrition shows low levels of Vitamin A. Numerous studies have found it to be protective against breast cancer.

- **Vitamin B Complex,** which is vital for the liver's breakdown of oestrogen. Also takes part in building a strong immune system and helps us deal with stressful situations.

- **Vitamin C.** Areas in the U.K., which show the lowest intake of Vitamin C and vegetables, have shown the highest incidence of breast cancer. However, it is important to discuss it with your doctor because Vitamin C supplements can interfere with some cancer drugs. It may possibly increase the risk of toxicity of the chemotherapy drug Methotrexate, hence it is advisable to avoid Vitamin C within twelve hours either side of taking this drug.

- **Vitamin E** supports the immune system's ability to respond to cancer. Studies have shown that blood levels are low in breast cancer patients. It can also be used to enhance the effects of conventional treatments and to reduce the toxic side effects. There was some controversy about the use of vitamin E in hormone-dependent cancers, because it was feared that it could have oestrogenic effect. However, this was before research, which has lead to the widespread view that phytoestrogens have a protective effect and are beneficial to cancer patients. Suggested dosage varies a great deal, Bristol recommends 400iu daily whereas other doctors recommend as much as 2,500iu on a daily basis. Precautions must be taken if anybody is taking warfarin, any other anti-coagulant drugs or asprin, because Vitamin E also has anti-coagulant properties. Dosage should therefore be discussed with doctor/consultant and regular blood tests should be taken, so that dosage of these drugs can be reduced, if necessary.

- **Selenium** is vital for glutathione peroxidase, which inhibits cell proliferation. Studies have revealed that areas with low selenium have higher rates of cancer (U.K. soil has very low levels). Selenium also effectively detoxifies the body of heavy metals and protects against environmental sensitivities and enhances the body's antibacterial and antiviral defences.

- **Zinc** is vital for a strong immune system, bone growth, appetite, vision and sexual functioning. It has been proven that artificial fertilisers lock up certain minerals in the soil, zinc and magnesium being the most notable. Insoluble compounds are formed, which vegetables are unable to absorb, causing mineral deficiencies in our diet.

- **Co-enzyme Q10** is a potent, fat-soluble antioxidant. Studies have shown that cancer patients have low levels of this. Interesting studies have shown that administration of Co Q10 has had some tantalizing effect in reversing breast cancer. It can also help to reduce cardiac toxicity from the chemotherapy drug Adriamycin. Unfortunately, it is an expensive supplement, however, it would appear that 100mg, as part of an overall synergistic antioxidant programme, has definite therapeutic effects.

- **Ultimate Oil Blend** delivers a balanced 2:1 ratio of Omega 3 to Omega 6. These are the source of two essential fats, linoleic acid and gamma-linoleic acid, which we have to include in our diet, because we are unable to manufacture them in our bodies, as we can other types of fat. Deficiency of them has serious health implications, as would vitamin deficiency. It is also thought that the protective effect of Omega 3 reduces the risk of breast cancer.

- **Dehydro-epi-andosterone (D.H.E.A.)** It has been shown that women with a low level of D.H.E.A. are more susceptible towards breast cancer.

- **Melatonin** to boost immune system. This hormone is particularly important for women of menopausal age.

- **Aloe Vera** is a powerful detoxifier, antiseptic and tonic for the nervous system. It also has immune-boosting and anti-viral properties, probably due to its high concentration of mucopolysaccharides, one of which is known as acemannan. Lignins, enzymes and antiseptic agents plus vitamins, minerals, essential fats and amino acids are also present. Following research done by Drs. Jeffrey Bland and Peter Atherton it was found that adding aloe vera to the diet improved digestion, absorption and elimination all of which was important for me to achieve a 'peak immune system'.

- **Apricot Kernels** as a source of B17 which consists of molecules that produces glucuronic acid which results in a selective toxicity to cancer cells.

- **Bach Flower Remedies** take effect by treating the individual, not the symptoms. These helped give great support to my fight against the illness by addressing the emotional factors that are known to impede physical healing.

As another route of avoiding synthetic hormones, a water filter system has been fitted in the house because it is apparent that chemicals in our water have an oestrogenic effect, however this filter had been fitted a few years before my cancer was diagnosed. Where possible, I have avoided food wrapped in plastic because plastics also have oestrogenic properties.

Fat cells, in our bodies, also produce oestrogen, hence another important reason for avoiding obesity. Apparently, women who store fat around their waistline i.e. apple shaped have been shown to be at greater risk of breast cancer – I am a definite pear shape which goes to show that this fact isn't always true!

Exercise reduces oestrogen levels in the body and therefore reduces the risk of many cancers, particularly those that are hormone related. It also helps to circulate immune cells around the body whilst stimulating lymphatic drainage and the removal of toxins from the body. I therefore do my best to take regular exercise, which includes walking, cycling and swimming. Being outside also improves my vitamin status and remembering that cancer cells hate oxygen makes it all feel so worthwhile.

Making time for myself has helped revolutionize my ability of coping with cancer. Staying at The Bristol Centre confirmed the importance of practising relaxation, visualisation and meditation, all of which I have found fulfilling and rewarding.

Sleeping has also been important because my metabolic rate, blood pressure, temperature and pulse all fall during this time. My body releases toxins because sweat production increases during this time. Sleep is also very important to the immune system, because it is during this time that the pituitary gland steps up the production of a growth hormone, which in turn stimulates the thymus gland, so essential for T cell activity.

I know skin brushing is important and although a skin brush is present in my shower room, I keep forgetting to use it! However, please do your best to make this part of your daily routine. The reason for it's importance is because it assists lymphatic drainage, which is part responsible for clearing unwanted debris, toxins and metabolic wastes and bacteria from the tissues because this system does not have a pump to move it round, instead it is completely reliant on gravity or the action of muscles.

Remember that it is important whilst practising this technique to brush towards the heart.

As assistance towards lymphatic drainage, it is also important not to wear tight clothing as these may restrict the flow even further hence restricting vital drainage and the cleaning-up process. Remember Dr Schachter putting emphasis on tight under wired bras as a contributory factor towards breast cancer due to the build-up of toxic wastes in the breast tissue.

Approximately six years prior to my cancer diagnosis being made, I became aware that most deodorants stop perspiration, which is the natural method of excreting toxic substances, and also contain cancer-causing agents; hence, I stopped purchasing commercial deodorants. (Aluminium in deodorants increases the risk of Alzheimer's disease).

Worwood V.(1990) states "commercial deodorants contain aluminium salts which stops perspiration and yet aluminium is a poison which could be absorbed into the skin. Stopping this natural method of excreting toxic substances – which is what perspiration does – is as silly as putting a stop on the other natural methods of excretion. It is bound to lead to trouble. The pores under your arms need to breathe and so try to avoid deodorants as much as possible."

Phillip Day (2000) states "Do not use anti-perspirants EVER AGAIN, as the aluminium and other compounds block up your lymph nodes, giving rise to major problems down the road when internal toxins can be driven back into the body, denied any means of escape and damage the lymph and breast. Remember, the idea is to get everything moving both inside and outside the body."

Further research revealed that shampoos, hair conditioner, body lotion, talc and other toiletries may contain carcinogens.......not forgetting the make-up that is applied afterwards.

"Talc is widely recognised to be the leading cause of ovarian cancer" states Phillip Day (2000).

Dr. Lee (1996) states "Statistically, we know that your risk of ovarian cancer increases if you use talcum powder. (It is thought that the powder, which contains toxins such as heavy metals, actually migrates up the vagina, through the cervix and into the uterus and ovaries)," in his book "Natural Progesterone."

I remember it being believed that the skin had a one-way function – it let sweat and toxins out of the body and acted like an impermeable raincoat i.e. a barrier that didn't allow anything in. However, that way of thinking has changed and it has been proven that many things are delivered via the skin.

It is horrifying to realize that 'dressing up' our appearance can be endangering our lives in a rather profound way. Fortunately, I have only ever used small amounts of make-up and perfume, and since my awareness of the dangers, those used are mostly of organic origin. However, many cosmetic ingredients are published in Latin hence they are difficult to decipher. Books are available that explain what the ingredients are, what they do and whether any risks are known: *Cosmetics Unmasked by Dr. Stephen and Gina Antczak and A Consumer's Dictionary of Cosmetic Ingredients by Ruth Winter, or The Safe Shopper's Bible by David Steinman and Samuel S. Epstein.*

You may also like to consider making your own, this is one foolproof way of being able to incorporate more high quality botanical ingredients. If you have the time and interest it will also save you money.

I feel pleased to know that a special Soil Association committee are currently drawing up regulations on organic health and beauty products. It is hoped that standards will be published later this year and a symbol should start appearing on a wider range of packaging. Currently, only one per cent of a cosmetic needs to be natural in order to qualify for the 'natural' label. This hardly seems fair, does it?

Exposure to chemicals in toiletries and cosmetics is only a small part of the overall chemical load encountered each day. Items such as cleaning products and garden chemicals may all have an impact on human health and wellbeing as well as the planet's.

Being careful about what is put in my mouth should not be undone by putting 'rubbish' on my skin, because 60% of this is absorbed into my body, hence when using cleaning products or gardening I always try to remember to protect myself by wearing gloves.

In general, we need to keep being reminded that the chemicals and preservatives in our environment have significant impact on our health.

Make yourself more aware of the ingredients in cosmetics and try to avoid ones containing Sodium Lauryl Sulphate, Sodium Laureth Sulfate and Propylene Glycol.

Due to my profession many people had to be informed of my illness, because I had to explain why I was unable to practise therapies for a while. This was not difficult for me and the reaction from clients gave me added strength to assist recovery.

The choice of whom to tell about your illness is entirely yours. Do what feels right – you must be totally honest with yourself, be careful not to undermine your own emotional well being because this will have effect on your recovery.

Positive thinking and laughter are also good for my emotional condition, hence I do my best to put them into practise on a daily basis.

During the latter years of my nursing career, there was a poem on display outside one of the bathrooms entitled 'smiling.' Before the hospital closed I decided to photocopy it and now find that I am able to visualise it, which in turn brings a smile to my face leading on to many pleasant memories of nursing at Black Notley Hospital, which no longer stands. I thought I would now like to take the opportunity of sharing the poem with you, my readers.

SMILING

Smiling is infectious
You catch it like the flu.
When someone smiled at me today
I started smiling too!

I passed around the corner
And someone saw my grin
When he smiled, I realised
I'd passed it onto him!

I thought about the smile
And then I realised its worth
A single smile like mine
Could travel round the earth.

If you feel a smile begin
Don't leave it undetected
Let's start an epidemic quick
And get the world infected!

Author unknown

Despite the seriousness of this illness, I have managed to overcome the black side of it and see a lot of white instead. The word 'cancer' no longer has a 'BIG C' it has been put into perspective and small letters all the way through is quite adequate. I feel a desire to support others who are going through similar states of shock on being diagnosed.

Because diet, relaxation and exercise are the parts of cancer treatment that we are all able to manage for ourselves I would like to share some more useful information towards a healthy diet with you, yet recommend that you purchase two books published by B.C.H.C. entitled *Healing Foods* and *Healing Foods Cookbook* which I have found to be very useful referral books. *Food For Thought* compiled by *Phillip Day* identifies the key truths of the body's requirements for food, water and air and includes recipes, which help give variation.

A poor diet will reduce the amount of oxygen available to the body tissues, making them more vulnerable to attack. Because cancer cells survive more effectively than healthy cells without oxygen, poor nutrition will allow cancer cells to proliferate. A diet that brings increased oxygen supply to the blood and body tissue will stimulate the immune system in order to attack and eliminate a tumour.

In the research that I have done it would appear that many people that have managed to overcome cancer have also made profound changes in their eating habits when diagnosed with cancer.

In general, saturated, trans and hydrogenated fats should be avoided. This includes cakes, sweets, biscuits, snacks like crisps etc. and processed foods. There is also scientific evidence that shows people who consume burnt, barbecued and smoked food run a greater risk of developing cancer because of the harmful free oxidising radicals that are present. Healthy, unsaturated, fats (Omega 6 and Omega 3) need to be consumed instead. They are needed for many different body functions including hormone production and balance, cell membrane structure and nerve tissue. Some of the main sources are oily fish, seeds, nuts and oils.

When cancer has started to develop it will feed directly on blood glucose, hence thrive in sugar-rich environments that will be created by a diet that is high in refined sugars. This is a good reason for eliminating them from your diet.

Soya has been shown to contain anti-cancer compounds, and should therefore be included in the daily diet regime. It can be taken in many ways, such as in the form of milk or yoghurt, as a drink or on cereals. Soya beans or tofu may be used in casseroles, soups etc.

Miso provides anti cancer properties without any of the chemicals often found in stock cubes. It is a brown paste made with a cultured grain base and fermented, which can be stored in the fridge, and used as a flavouring in soups and stews. Tempeh (cultured beancurd) can also be used in the same way.

These products should preferably be of organic culture.

Another good reason for the inclusion of soya in the diet regime is because it is known to help reduce toxic side effects of radiation and chemotherapy.

The brassica family, or cruciferous vegetables, includes broccoli, cauliflower, cabbage, brussels sprouts, kale, horseradish, radishes, swede and turnip. These are proving to be anti-cancer vegetables of the moment. They contain several potentially anti-carcinogenic, bioactive micronutrients. Indole-3-carbinol is one that is of particular interest in human studies because it encourages deactivation of oestrogens.

Broccoli also has a good calcium content – a generous sized head contains more calcium than a cup of milk.

Foods rich in beta-carotene, particularly carrots, are also thought to be very protective against cancer. Carrots should be included in the diet on a daily basis. "They should be cooked, in order to achieve more anti-cancer properties" is stated in part 1 of 'eat for immunity' printed by The Daily Mail. Cooking releases carotenes, believed to be active agents in shielding body tissues against carcinogenic attacks. Cooking carrots increases the amount of carotene released 2-5 fold. Overcooking must also be avoided, otherwise much beta-carotene is lost.

Tomatoes contain a carotenoid-lycopene (red pigment). Studies show that eating a diet rich in tomatoes helps reduce the risks of developing various forms of cancer and heart disease. Lycopene is a powerful antioxidant that picks up free radicals in the body. The National Cancer

Institute published a study, which showed that men consuming high levels of tomato products reduced their risk of prostate cancer by 35%. There is also some thought that lycopene consumption reduces the risk of cancers of the breast, cervix, mouth, stomach, lung, mouth, pancreas, oesophagus, colon and rectum. Research also shows that lycopene is more efficiently absorbed by the body, if the tomatoes are processed. So remember to add juice, purée, and tinned tomatoes to your shopping list. Still try to go easy on the ketchup, because of the sugar and salt being added.

Avocados are another source of beta-carotene, yet also contain high levels of vitamin E and glutathione, which is a powerful anti-oxidant that attacks cancer-causing agents. Potassium is also present which is beneficial if suffering from sluggishness, fatigue or depression, all symptoms, of which, may go hand in hand with cancer.

Grapes are a storehouse of antioxidant, anti-cancer compounds. They possess high levels of a strong anti-cancer compound known as ellagic acid. Red grapes (not green) are high in the antioxidant quercetin. Anti bacterial and antiviral properties are also present. "Grapes have anti-mutagenic properties and may be particularly good at preventing breast cancers which arise with age." States Suzannah Oliver (1999) in her book "The Breast Cancer Prevention and Recovery Diet."

Grape crops do tend to be excessively sprayed in the vineyards, it is therefore wise to buy organic brands when able, otherwise, be sure to wash them well before consumption.

Raisins are dried grapes and therefore give a concentrated form of the grape's nutrients and also rich in tannins and caffeic acid.

Dried fruits are good energy providers as well as being packed with iron, potassium, selenium, fibre, vitamins and minerals, so are therefore good convenience snacks in moderation.

Apples also have an abundancy of caffeic acid and may be consumed raw, cooked or juiced.

Watermelons are another good source of antioxidant and anti-cancer compounds – lycopene and glutathione. They also contain high amounts of vitamin C – one large slice contains 80% of recommended daily allowance and beta-carotene is also present.

Citrus fruits contain D-limonene (specially found in the oil from the skin of the fruit, hence use organic, not waxed) which inhibits mammary cancer. In animal studies this compound brought advanced mammary cancer to a halt, which appears remarkable. Liver detoxification enzymes are also enhanced by limonene. This helps remove carcinogens from the body. The bitter white pith is a potent source of bioflavonoids which complement the vitamin C found in the fruit which enhances the potency. Pectin is also present in the pith, which helps detoxify the body. Red grapefruit is another source of lycopene.

Citrus fruits are also effective energy boosters and aid healing by strengthening bones, blood vessels and other tissues.

Berries are rich in flavonoids and anthocyanins which have anti-cancer properties.

Garlic and onions, like other sulphur foods help the liver detoxify the toxins. While garlic is quite harmless to 'normal' cells it is quite toxic to cancer cells. Allicin is one of the active ingredients responsible for this, and helps enhance the immune system.

It also stimulates the T-cells to help fight cancer. Not only does it protect against the formation of tumours, including metastases, it also inhibits the growth of established tumours. The National Cancer Institute in the U.S.A. recognises garlic as a preventive against cancer, because it has been shown clinically to inhibit the growth of breast cancer.

Linseeds, Wheat Bran, Oat Bran, Sunflower, Sesame and Pumpkin Seeds: These are all high in lignans which help lower oestrogen dominance, hence reduce risks of hormone related cancers. Linseeds are the richest source.

Wheatgrass for vibrant health. It is purported to contain more than 100 vitamins, minerals and nutrients, 60 times more Vitamin C than oranges, 8 times more iron than spinach, all of the eight essential amino acids plus 11 more, polypeptides and the bioflavenoids believed to neutralise toxic substances in the blood. It, therefore, enhances the immune system, is a powerful liver detoxifier, stimulates the production of haemoglobin and helps regulate blood-fat levels.

Wheatgrass is also an overall energising tonic. The only problem is wheatgrass is not very easy to obtain and is expensive. However, you can grow your own, for a reasonable price, and add it to salads and sandwiches. Some health shops sell it in powder form, which can be added to your drinks.

Fresh, (organically grown, if possible) nuts are good sources of protease inhibitors, essential fats and antioxidants. Almonds are a good source of laetrile. They are also rich in vitamin B2 which helps clear your liver of excess oestrogens. Walnuts are a good source of vitamins, particularly B6, and minerals. However, make sure that they are fresh because rancid ones can be carcinogenic!

Remember though that all nuts have a high calorie and fat content, although the fat is mostly unsaturated, they should still be eaten in moderation.

Unfortunately, some foods are said to be carcinogenic (increase the risk of cancer) – so please do your best to avoid these, or at least reduce the amount consumed wherever possible – caffeine, additives, salt, smoked food, foods containing nitrites/nitrates, e.g. ham, bacon, sausages, non-organic produce, burnt food, barbecued food, foods wrapped in plastic, microwaved foods in plastic containers.

Fizzy/sweetened drinks – the consumption of these has greatly increased over the past ten to fifteen years so that many children are not aware of drinking water as we always used to. Nowadays, it is 'the norm' for many households to take in an extra 1,000 calories daily through 'fizzy pop drinks,' milk shakes and sugar added to tea and coffee. These are 'empty calories' there is no nutritional value and obesity is the side effect.

A glass of pure fruit juice goes towards your daily consumption of five servings of fruit and vegetables. However, whenever possible it is best to make your own, because many shop bought ones have been heat-treated hence lost much of the goodness, so of course, some are better than others – perhaps 'you get what you pay for'.

Try to cut out tea and coffee because of the stimulant properties. I used to love drinking coffee and never thought I would consider stopping it. Thinking back to my nurse training days we were always consuming coffee. I asked for a percolator as a birthday present and thought it was lovely to have the permanent aroma of coffee in the nurse's home, and I thought nothing of consuming 6-8 mugs per day.

Now that I realise coffee contains other stimulants – theobromine and theophyline - as well as caffeine which have potent effects on the body i.e. over stimulation of the adrenal glands leading to blood sugar swings - I have not found it difficult to stop drinking coffee routinely and just enjoy the occasional one socially.

The fact that coffee also decreases the absorption of nutrients from food by up to 20% means that I cannot afford to drink much because food is my medicine!

Rachel Charles, in her book 'Mind, Body and Immunity' states "Coffee inhibits the absorption of zinc, so vital for immunity" then goes on to tell of different research studies showing that regular coffee consumption increases the risk of cancer development.

I also appreciate that coffee enemas are sometimes prescribed to help the liver detoxify. I understand that the theory behind this is that the coffee travels straight to the liver, via the portal vein, causing it to speed up the elimination of toxins that have been stored. However, I have not done any research on this subject but understand that some people have found this procedure very effective.

Tea is also high in caffeine, yet because we tend to make a much weaker solution, approximately 50% less is taken, but of course, tannin needs to be considered.

However, there are many teas that have antioxidant properties, particularly green tea which has been shown to be very protective against cancer and only has half as much caffeine as black tea.

This type of tea is made from the fresh tips, whereas the leaves used for black tea are withered and oxidised. Oxidisation will have destroyed some of the tannins, which have strong antibacterial and antiviral properties. Polyphenols are some of the chemicals present in green tea, which are thought to have anti-cancer properties.

Professor Jane Plant (2000) states, "It is thought that the well known anti-cancer activity of green tea is because it inhibits one of the most frequently over-exposed enzymes in human cancers, called urokinase."

So perhaps you should just consider changing the brand of tea that you use for a green tea instead and try drinking it black, without milk.

Other teas to consider drinking are Mu tea and Rooibosch. What about herbal teas? These may be consumed cold as well as hot. Consider making a large jug of it, which can be stored in the fridge, in the summer time. This can then be enjoyed as a cold drink instead of 'squashes' that have a high sugar content.

When I was breastfeeding Thomas I found that he was unable to tolerate dairy products, hence I started drinking black tea. Then, if anybody offered me tea with milk, it repulsed me, so, this just goes to show how our 'taste buds' change.

Many people do not give water intake much thought, yet it is the second most essential nutrient needed by the body, following air. Our human bodies are composed of approximately 75% water and 25% solids, whilst brain tissue is said to consist of 85% water.

Approximately between one and a half and two litres of water are eliminated from the body each day in the form of urine, sweat, digestion, detoxifying and our breathing so, obviously this needs to be replaced.

Before chemotherapy and following the drug administration (prior to vomiting starting) I would drink excess water in order to eliminate the by-products as soon as possible.

The quality of water is also important, filtered is preferable.

Chemicals in our drinking water, causing an oestrogenic effect, is questionable. Bottled water varies dramatically. Read the ingredients label before purchasing – some have very high sodium (salt) content. Glass bottles are also preferable, because plastic is a source of oestrogenic nonylphenols which leach into the water. 'Spring water' is also misleading. One generally visualises lovely clear springs in the countryside, but don't forget it can include well water from agricultural areas that have been directly exposed to environmental chemicals, pesticides etc.

Alcohol depletes the immune boosting nutrients, particularly glutathione which is important in fighting cancer and for liver detoxification. Whilst actively fighting cancer, or undergoing chemotherapy it should be avoided, otherwise the liver would become overloaded, hence reducing the ability to breakdown excess oestrogen and other toxins.

As you probably are aware, there are different reports, for and against, the consumption of alcohol. Some say that small quantities stimulate the production of prostaglandin E1 (an important part of immune function) hence two or three measures of red wine per week pre-menopausal, or one measure a day post-menopausal (if not taking H.R.T.) may be beneficial. Whereas other reports state that even social drinking can increase the risk of cancer – percentages vary from 27 to 100%. 100% means that it doubles your risk! Also, contrary to popular belief regular consumption does raise anxiety levels.

I never consumed any in the acute stage, now I enjoy the odd one socially.

I was also pleased to read in Suzannah Olivier's book that chocolate wasn't all bad. "It does contain useful amounts of magnesium and phenol antioxidants." I do appreciate though that it is another source of caffeine and empty calories. I refrained from it completely during the acute stage, now I will enjoy a small amount very occasionally (whereas, many years ago I thought nothing of eating one half pound bar of fruit and nut chocolate most evenings!) Now, I try to go more towards good-quality, organic, dark chocolate when able. However, along with changing habits the same desire for chocolate is no longer there.

Seriously though, sugar is described as 'pure, white and deadly'- there is no goodness in refined sugar at all. Are you aware of the 'hidden sugar' in processed foods? Manufacturers are putting more sugar into products, such as baked beans, tomato sauce and beef burgers, possibly the sort of food you would never think of containing sugar – look at the labels, particularly if they are advertised as 'low fat.' Until recently only half our consumption of sugar came from this kind of source. "Now two thirds of the sugar we eat comes loaded into foods like canned sweetcorn, breakfast cereals and soft drinks" states C. Wright (1998).

Sugar can have a positively harmful effect on the body as the digestive system struggles to deal with it, and C. Wright (1998) states "sugar can have real and damaging effects on mood and behaviour that are now too well documented to be doubted."

This might mean changing your eating habits. If you eat regular wholesome meals 'comfort eating' will fall away. If you have the need for mid-meal snacks try fresh fruit, dried fruit, unsalted nuts or seeds such as pumpkin and sunflower. Sometimes we feel irritated because our fluid intake is low, so try a glass of filtered water, because dehydration increases the levels of toxins in the blood.

If you have been eating processed foods for a long time, you may find it difficult to switch straight over to wholemeal bread, pasta, brown rice etc. In these conditions try doing it gradually, e.g. make a sandwich with one brown slice and one white slice, use 50% brown rice 50% white, rather than the ordeal of a sudden change. You will also find that this looks more attractive on the plate.

There are also plenty of substitutes you can use in cooking, for sweetening properties, such as apple juice, fruit puree, date syrup or maple syrup, as you will see in some of my recipes that follow.

I must add how my taste buds have changed though. It is quite surprising how one adapts to different eating habits. I feel sure many of you readers can confirm that from your own experience of following different diets for various reasons. Now, more often than not, after the consumption of a small amount of chocolate I ask myself "Why did I crave for that?" It will often leave a strange feeling in my mouth and sometimes my stomach area feels uncomfortable 20-40 minutes later.

Too much salt isn't good for us. Large amounts have been used in modern food processing which has accustomed many people to expect a salty taste when eating savoury foods. There is no need to add table salt and one can try experimenting with other forms of seasoning, such as miso, shoyu, tamari, herbs, ground seaweed or potassium-based salt substitute. Remember to look out for low-salt labels on stock cubes/powder etc.

Read ingredients labels because salt is used in sweet products as well – many brands of cornflakes use twice the amount of salt, in proportion, as most brands of potato crisps.

Eat more raw foods – aim for a 50-50 ratio of raw to cooked. This can have a significant effect on raising energy levels and improving the functioning of our body tissues. Potassium is also found in abundance in raw, unprocessed plant foods – Max Gerson advocated high potassium and it is from his work that much of our understanding of the role that diet plays in the treatment of cancer has arisen. Enzymes are an absolutely essential part of anticancer treatment.

Cancer cells thrive in oxygen free environments. Good nutrition will help to defeat them by ensuring that all body tissues are well oxygenated.

Generally, avoid foods that are difficult to digest, the body will then have more energy to fight the 'naughty' cells – i.e. a diet that demands the least gives the most.

It has certainly helped me a great deal.

Recipes

Making changes to your diet can sometimes cause panic. To prove it can be done without too much fuss I thought I would give you a few examples of easy ways to adapt meals to meet your dietary demands and I have listed some recipe books that I found helpful.

Textured soya protein (TVP) is a dehydrated product made from soya flour, and formed into shapes, which can be reconstituted with boiling water and used in any number of dishes instead of meat and provide the benefits of soya beans.

Instead of using minced beef in recipes such as Bolognese sauce, lasagne, burgers I use soya, quorn mince or red lentils. Soya chunks can replace stewing steak and quorn pieces may be used instead of chicken.

Organically grown products are more beneficial to use and it is now a lot easier to find them on supermarket shelves. Although it is more expensive, think of the money you may be saving from the meat counter.

Nitrates are frequently used as preservatives and convert to nitrites. In turn, these develop into nitrosamines which are potent carcinogens. So this is another good reason for going organic.

Don't worry about it too much if you can't, because it is impossible to control our whole environment. Do the best you can to enjoy it and remember 'we are what we eat.'

Because lycopene is an important ingredient, here are a few recipes that I enjoy, rich in tomatoes.

Gazpacho

2 cloves of garlic
1 medium onion
500g tomatoes
1 sml. cucumber
1 green pepper
750ml tomato juice
200g roughly cubed
wholemeal bread

4 tbsps. Olive oil
1 rounded tbsp. tomato puree
4tbsps. wine vinegar
oregano and basil
freshly ground blackpepper

Cover tomatoes with boiling water for 30 secs. Remove skin and roughly chop the flesh. Peel and crush the garlic. Peel and chop onion and cucumber. Remove stalk and seeds from pepper; roughly chop flesh.

Put garlic, tomatoes, onion, cucumber, green pepper, bread and 500ml tomato juice into a bowl and stand for 10 mins. Then liquidise. Blend oil and tomato puree together, then add to mixture with vinegar and herbs. Season to taste and add remaining tomato juice.

Chill thoroughly.

This may be served with croutons and chopped vegetables, such as peppers, carrots and cucumbers.

Tomato Ring

1x 397g. can tomatoes
150ml. Tomato juice
Agar agar
6 tbsps. French dressing

2 cloves garlic
1 bouquet garni
pepper
basil, fresh or dried

Salad

6 tomatoes, skinned, seeded
and chopped
1/2 sml. red onion

1/4 cucumber, diced
1/2 green pepper, cored
seeded and chopped

Place can of tomatoes, garlic, tomato juice and bouquet garni in a saucepan and bring slowly to the boil. Simmer for 5mins. Discard bouquet garni and season.

Place in liquidiser with agar agar and blend for approx 30secs.

Add 4 tbsps. of the dressing and 1/2 the salad ingredients and stir well. Pour into a greased ring mould and chill in the refrigerator until set (approx. 3hours).

Turn out onto a serving plate and place the remaining salad ingredients, mixed with the remaining dressing, in the centre.

Guiness is a good source of Vitamin B, iron and folic acid. Some people have said that a bottle a day helps improve the blood count. This means it could reduce the chance of not being able to receive chemotherapy treatment. I find it difficult to tolerate as a drink, therefore hoped that using it in cooking may have proved beneficial.

Guiness Casserole

2 tbsps. olive oil	320g mushrooms, sliced
350g baby onions	2 crushed cloves of garlic
2 sticks celery, chopped	225g carrots, cut into chunks
1 swede, cut into chunks	2 parsnips, cut into chunks
2tbsps. plain flour	600ml vegetable stock
450ml guiness	2 tbsps. tomato purée
3tbsps. chopped fresh thyme	seasoning

For the topping

2 large potatoes, thinly sliced
soya spread

Preheat oven to 200C, Gas Mark 6

Heat 1 tbsp. of oil in large saucepan/frying pan, add mushrooms and fry for a few minutes 'til brown. Transfer to casserole dish.

Heat remaining oil and stir in the garlic, onions, celery, carrots, swede and parsnip and cook for a further few minutes. Return mushrooms to the pan.

Sprinkle the flour over the vegetables and cook for 1 minute. Pour in the stock, guiness, tomato puree and thyme. Season well, bring to the boil and simmer for 10 minutes.

Transfer to casserole dish. Arrange potato slices over the top.

Cover and bake in the oven for 20 minutes.

Remove the lid, dot potato slices with soya spread. Return to oven and bake for approx. 15 mins. until top is browned and vegetables are tender.

Millet Bake

Many years ago, a friend asked 'what is on the menu for dinner tonight?'

When I answered "Millett Bake" she laughed at me and said that millet was 'birdseed.' Several years on I discovered that millet is a good source of B17, hence 'thought you might like to try this recipe.

200g millet	1litre vegetable stock
1 bayleaf	mixed herbs
2 tbsps sunflower oil	1 lge onion, chopped
2 carrots, finely chopped	1sml red pepper, chopped
1 clove of garlic, crushed	50g mushrooms, sliced
2 tsps coriander powder	2 tbsps tamari sauce
2 tbsps chopped fresh parsley	Grated rind of ½ lemon
1 dstsp Arrowroot	Seasoning

Topping
4 tomatoes, sliced   Olive oil

Dry roast the millet. Remove from the heat, add 750ml of stock, stir and bring to the boil. Add the herbs and cover tightly. Cook over a low heat until the liquid is absorbed and the millet is tender – approx. 25 mins.- extra water may be added, if necessary.

Heat the sunflower oil in another pan and gently fry the onion and carrot with the lid on. When softened, add the red pepper and garlic. Cook for a further few minutes. Lastly, stir in the mushrooms and coriander, cook briefly then add remaining stock. Blend the arrowroot with a little cold water then add to vegetables to thicken the fluid. Set aside.

Remove the bayleaf from the cooked millet and mix well with the vegetable sauce. Add tamari sauce, parsley, lemon rind and pepper.

Grease an ovenproof dish and spoon in the mixture. Arrange sliced tomatoes over the top and drizzle with olive oil.

Bake in a hot oven Gas Mk 4 / 180degrees C. for approx. 20 mins.

Serve hot with lemony mushroom sauce, steamed broccoli and/or side salad.

Lemony Mushroom Sauce

250ml vegetable stock
1 tsp. Arrowroot
2 spring onions, finely chopped
2 tsps. lemon juice
Black pepper
Grated nutmeg

1 dstsp. Tamari
1 dstsp. Sunflower oil
50g button mushrooms, sliced

Heat the oil and fry the onion and mushrooms for a few minutes. Stir in the lemon juice, stock and tamari. Bring to the boil and simmer for 5 mins.

Blend the arrowroot to a smooth paste with a little cold water.

Remove pan from the heat and blend paste into the mixture, stirring all the time. Bring back to the boil, stirring. Simmer for 1-2 minutes until clear and thickened. Add pepper and nutmeg to taste.

Millet and Seed Loaf

1 cup millet
1 medium onion
2 tomatoes
Sml. tin chopped tomatoes
2 tbsps. soya flour
Mixed herbs
1 tbsp. olive oil

3/4 cup mixed seeds e.g.
linseed, sunflower etc.
(crushed apricot kernels may
 also be included)
1 tbsp. rice flour
Freshly ground black pepper

Pre heat oven to 190degrees C / Gas mk. 5. Oil a loaf tin and line with greaseproof paper.

Wash millet. Cover with water and bring to the boil. Leave to simmer for approx. 20-30 mins. 'til water is absorbed.

Grind the seeds. Heat the oil and gently soften the chopped onion, in a covered pan. Mix all ingredients together, adding enough fluid to obtain a sticky mixture.

Slice the tomatoes and spread them over the base of the loaf tin. Put the mixture on top and press down firmly.

Bake for approx. 35 mins. 'til firm. Leave to stand for a few minutes, then turn out of tin and remove greaseproof paper. Serve hot or cold.

Lentil Stew

This recipe is very adaptable. It may be served as it is with mashed potatoes, or wholemeal bread. Otherwise it can be served as a sauce with pasta (thickened with a blend of cornflour, if needed) or layered with sheets of wholewheat lasagne, a 'topping' added and baked in the oven.

I, therefore, sometimes make twice the quantity to save time and adapt it to different dishes. It also freezes well. This can make life easier on the days you have less time or energy.

2 onions, chopped
4 celery sticks, chopped
1 bay leaf
800ml. water
Freshly ground black pepper
Parsley, to garnish

4 carrots, chopped
2 cloves of garlic, crushed
2 cans chopped tomatoes
275g red lentils, washed
chopped parsley, oregano
and basil

Put all ingredients, except ground pepper and herbs, in a large saucepan and bring to the boil. Simmer for approx 45mins 'til lentils and veggies are tender. Add chopped herbs and pepper to taste. Serve, as desired, garnished with parsley.

Soya Goulash

100g soya chunks
100g potatoes, peeled and chopped
1 lge onion, chopped
1 lge can chopped tomatoes
2 bay leaves
2 tsps cornflour

100g carrots, chopped
1 red pepper, deseeded and chopped
2 cloves of carlic, crushed
500ml vegetable stock
1 dstsp. Paprika

Pre heat oven to170 degrees C / Gas mk.4

Put soya chunks in casserole dish and cover with boiling water. Leave to stand for ten minutes. Add remaining ingredients, except cornflour. Put into oven for approx. 1hr 'til vegetables are tender.

Blend cornflour with a little cold water, then stir into goulash to give the required consistency.   Serve with cooked brown rice and side salad.

Rice Salad

350g. cooked brown rice

3 tbsps. chopped macadamia nuts

½ orange pepper, chopped

1 tsp. toasted fennel seeds

1 tsp. toasted cumin seeds

6 fresh apricots, chopped

4 spring onions, sliced

2 tbsps. tamari

3 tbsps. olive oil

3 tbsps. lemon juice

Mix all these ingredients together and leave to stand for 1hr, to enable flavours to 'melt' together.

We still like to have a tea-time treat yet shop-bought cakes are not at all good for you. Not only do they have high sugar and fat content, refined white flour is normally used.

I have, therefore chosen these 'sweet treats' to share with you, which contain essential vitamins and minerals.

Fruit and Seed Squares

80g dried apricots

125ml sunflower oil

25g sunflower seeds

1 dstsp. Apricot kernels, crushed (optional)

100g raisins

200g porridge oats

25g linseeds

Soak the dried apricots for a few hours in cold water, blend to a paste. Mix all the ingredients together – in a food processor, if so desired.

Press mixture into a prepared swiss roll tin and smooth the top with a spatula.

Bake for 30 mins in a pre-heated oven 180degrees C / gas 4.

Cool in tin for 5 mins., then cut into squares and remove to a cooling rack., before being stored in an airtight tin.

Chewy Bars

If you are following a diet that allows 'fruit only' until midday this is a good mid-morning snack with a herbal tea.

250g dried apricots

Cover with cold water and soak for a few hours. Liquidise with a small amount of the fluid. Cover a baking tin (approx. 22cm. square) with non-stick baking paper and spread fruit mixture evenly over it.

Bake in the oven, at very low heat, for approx. 6 hours to become dry and chewy.

Peel off the paper, cut into squares and store in the refrigerator.

Fruit Cake

2 bananas, mashed
110g raisins, sultanas, currants
2tbsps. chopped apricot kernels
150g wholemeal flour
4fl oz apple juice

1 pear, finely chopped
50g ground almonds
75g porridge oats
3fl oz sunflower oil

Heat oven to 190degrees C. / gas mark 5. Prepare 19cm cake tin.

Mix all ingredients together to reach a moist consistency. Spoon into cake tin.

Bake for approx. 45mins. until firm to touch and inserted skewer comes out clean. Let stand for a few mins. before turning out onto a cooling rack.

Fruit Crumble

250g Hunza apricots left to soak in orange juice for several hours

or

450g raspberries sweetened with concentrated apple juice

Topping

50g soya margarine	75g wholewheat flour
75g porridge oats	3 tbsps. sunflower oil
1 tbsp chopped apricot kernels	2 tbsps. concentrated fruit juice

Heat oven 180degrees C. / gas mark 4

Place fruit in a greased ovenproof dish. Pour in sufficient fluid to moisten.

Rub fat into flour. Add remaining ingredients and stir thoroughly.
Sprinkle over fruit and bake for 20-25 mins. until browned.

Poppy Seed Cake

Poppy seeds contain a staggering 1,200mg of calcium per 100g, so I hope you enjoy this cake as a means of supply.

100g/4oz blue poppy seeds	2 eggs
225ml/8fl.oz soya milk	225g/8oz wholemeal S.R.
225g/8oz soya margarine	flour
150g/6oz 100% pure fruit spread	

Pre heat oven to gas mk 4/180degrees C. Grease and line an 8" cake tin

Bring poppy seeds to the boil in the soya milk, then turn off the heat and leave them to soak for 25 mins in a covered pan.

Cream the margarine and fruit spread together until light and fluffy.
Beat the eggs and stir in gradually. Fold flour in, small amounts at a time.
Stir in poppy seed mixture and mix well together.
Spoon mixture into prepared tin and level the surface.
Bake for approximately 1 hour, or until centre feels firm.
Let cake stand for a few minutes before turning onto a cooling rack and leave to cool.

As I mentioned before, my interest in food disappeared whilst undergoing chemotherapy treatment. When vomiting ceased, I would try to consume my nutrition in liquid form. This took less effort, and nicer still, it was often prepared for me.

Carrot and Broccoli Soup

1 tbsp. olive oil
4 garlic cloves, crushed
15fl oz / 500ml stock
4oz / 110g spinach
2tbsp parsley, chopped
Tabasco sauce (optional)

1 med. onion, chopped
1 carrot, chopped
12oz / 350g broccoli
1 tomato, chopped
black pepper

Wash and prepare vegetables.

Heat the oil in a large saucepan. Add the onion, garlic and carrot and sauté for approx. 5mins. 'til onion is tender. Add stock, broccoli, tomato and parsley.
Simmer 'til broccoli is tender – approx. 15mins.
Add spinach and cook, uncovered for a couple of minutes.
Allow to cool a little, then puree. Season to taste.

Fruit Smoothie

3oz / 85g strawberries or blueberries
½ pear, peeled & chopped
1tbsp sunflower & sesame seeds

4fl oz / 125ml organic soya
4fl oz / 125ml yofu milk

Combine all ingredients together in a liquidiser and puree.

Serve in a glass.

'Pick Me Up'

250 ml apple juice
½ oz / 15g wheatgerm

1 tbsp clear honey

Put all ingredients into blender and blend for 30secs.

Pour into glass and serve.

Tips for healthy immune system

A healthy immune system has the power to destroy cancer cells as they are formed. Here are some tips to keep yours in good shape.

1) Eat a healthy diet, including plenty of fresh (preferably organic) fruit and vegetables. Avoid all processed and convenience foods.

2) Drink only filtered or bottled water. Avoid milk, coffee, fizzy drinks and cordials.

3) Do not smoke. Avoid alcohol, if possible, otherwise keep in moderation, only 'drinking' occasionally.

4) Avoid taking drugs, especially antibiotics and steroids, unless essential. Overuse of antibiotics has been shown to damage the immune system, and many organisms are now themselves immune to them.

5) Exercise – don't make sudden changes. Sudden rigorous exercise should be avoided. Gentle regular exercise, extending yourself each day, will help metabolism, digestion, circulation and lymphatic systems. Depending on age, weight, state of health etc. movement, that increases the heartbeat sufficiently for approximately 20 mins. a day, can be extremely valuable. Just remember that cancer cells hate oxygen, hence increasing your intake will be very beneficial. The production of killer T-cells will also be increased.

6) Reduce Stress levels

My Celebration Party

One year on, with generally enjoying life to the full I decided to invite some friends to lunch as a token of thanks for their help and moral support.

Although I would have loved to invite Christine, because of her state of health, of course I couldn't. Instead, I raised a glass and my thoughts went out to her.

Two days later she quietly passed away into the next world. God Bless you, Christine.

Nurse friends from Black Notley - Hazel, Halima, Julie , Alison & Mandy

Future Outlook

The number of new cancer cases being diagnosed has steadily increased since the 1960s. Facts shown on the Internet state that each year in the U.K. around 35,000 new cases of breast cancer are diagnosed. About 14,000 of these ladies die. Breast cancer is the commonest single cause of death among women aged 35-54years.

Despite spending large amounts of money on cancer research, little progress has been made in conventional medicine to find safe and effective treatments.

Very large sums of money have been spent on cancer treatment alone. Most direct expenditures for cancer are attributable to breast, colorectal, lung and prostate cancer, in that order.

Spokespersons for conventional cancer care look upon a five-year survival rate as an indication of progress and money well spent. However, the quality of life isn't considered – many of these people are living a restricted lifestyle, some may even be bedridden for a large amount of the time. The facts are that five-year survival rates for cancers of the liver, lung, pancreas, bone and breast are about the same as they were in 1965.

Conventional oncologists use the five-year mark as a yardstick for "cure". It doesn't matter if one dies of cancer one day after the five-year mark, it is still counted among the cases cured. Since many people do die soon after five years, this can be a highly misleading statistic! For example, the five-year survival rate for breast cancer is 75%, yet survival beyond this is less than 50%. Likewise, five-year survival rate for prostate cancer is 70% while ten-year survival drops to 35%.

'Success' only exists on paper. Because diagnosis may be made earlier these days due to the introduction of new diagnostic equipment, it makes survival time appear longer than in the past. For example, because, on average, a woman's breast cancer may be diagnosed three years earlier because of mammography, she may live for seven years, whereas if older diagnostic tools had been used, this same person would be shown in statistics to have only lived for four years.

"Cures" are often referred to in orthodox medicine, yet they prohibit complementary practitioners from ever using the word. Curing typically refers to medical treatment that relieves the patient of the disease. By contrast, 'healing' refers to an internal process of "becoming whole" – a feeling of harmonious relationship with one's entire environment.

The aims of complementary therapies are to boost the patient's own self-healing properties whilst avoiding toxic side effects that accompany standard cancer treatment. Most doctors, practising alternative treatments, start with a positive attitude and advise the patient to make dietary changes. By helping to rejuvenate the 'whole' person, these strategies also offer an improved quality of life and a sense of control in the healing process.

Dr. Ernesto R. Contreras, M.D., who graduated as a surgeon and physician in 1939 from the Army Medical School in Mexico City, held various academic and professional positions including general practitioner and professor of histology and pathology.

In 1963, he founded Oasis Hospital in Tijuana and he has served there since as chief oncologist and general director. It is his policy to treat his patients holistically and he quotes "This approach is made possible only when physicians are willing to use a special blend of science, medicine, faith and compassion to make a vital and lasting connection with the patient."

He also quotes "A person's positive attitude and faith bring about favourable chemical changes in the body that ward off offending cancer-causing chemical messengers."

Dr. Contreras supports that a positive approach is therapeutic, which explains the reason that optimists live longer.

Conventional cancer treatments are in place as law of the land because they *pay*, not heal, the best. To the cancer establishment, cancer patients are looked upon as a profit centre! Of course, the politics-of-cancer will keep this away from you and will continue to do so while able. Wake up to reality and question treatment that is prescribed.

Phillip Day (2000) supports my feelings by stating "Of course, true and responsible medicine has a part to play in our society today – no question of it. Every time I fell off my motorcycle as a teenager, I was grateful to the Accident and Emergency Unit for stitching me back together again with great skill, a kind word and some marvellous coffee. Certain ailments are best treated in our hospitals – who would argue? But when is enough enough? Is it when medicine ceases to be for the good of the patient and begins operating for the good of the shareholder? If it is, we are way past that point today, and our health industries have become ever more cynical and manipulative in their dealings with their patients' misery and weakness as time progresses."

The treatment path I followed cost so much less, more people could have been treated, yet, because of the pharmaceutical industries need for profit and the conservatism of the medical establishment my funding was out of the question. I had to fund it myself.

Does this make sense?

At one of the seminars I attended Ralph Moss Ph.D., shared some of his experience of working for Memorial Sloan-Kettering Hospital with us. He informed us of some of the shady history of this cancer establishment and how he was fired in 1977 for refusing to cover up favourable research data on laetrile. In 1987 Memorial Sloan-Kettering owned almost 70,000 shares in 7 major pharmaceutical companies.

In Phillip Day's book 'Health Wars' He states that Dr. Ralph Moss states "In the end, there is no proof that chemotherapy in the vast majority of cases actually extends life, and this is the GREAT LIE about chemotherapy, that somehow there is a correlation between shrinking a tumour and extending the life of a patient."

In "Cancer. Why We're Still Dying To Know The Truth." Phillip Day refers to a radio interview with Ralph Moss when he stated "We were finding that Laetrile was having a positive effect, yet we in Public Affairs were told to issue statements to the exact opposite of what we were finding scientifically."

The opposition of the cancer industry to laetrile (amygdalin or Vit. B17), derived mainly from apricot kernels and many other fruit pips, is only one example in a long, depressing saga of big business colluding with the government to suppress therapeutic and commercial alternatives.

In Health Wars (2001) Phillip Day states "we are about to find out that both heart disease and cancer can end today based entirely on existing scientific knowledge. That is why I become increasingly tired of the whining British National Health Service and it's government over cash shortages in Britain and how financially strapped the hospitals and health services are today. None of this would be happening if the population and its health services WOULD EXERCISE PREVENTION INSTEAD OF CURE. For who, in reality, is responsible for the soaring costs of healthcare today, if not we, the population, through not taking proper care of ourselves (our responsibility, not the government's)?

And how about the pharmaceutical industry, for overcharging for their dubious and dangerous 'cures' to fill the increased demand, all the while we become not only obstinate about changing our wicked ways, but never more abandoned in our lifestyle and food habits as time moves on. Make no mistake about it. When you hear the financial creaking of a health service, like we hear sounding in Britain, what you are witnessing is a sickness dynamo that has succeeded in generating profits beyond it's architects' wildest imaginations."

Cancer charities that ask for donations claim that further research will be done to save lives. Research continues, keeping certain people occupied and well paid, yet no complete cure is ever developed. Why don't they do more towards prevention in the first place? Could it be because this field is a lot less profitable? Treating cancer is now a big business, with multi million dollar annual cancer drug sales, hence they continue to operate, no matter what the ethics are of the methods involved.

Having had the experience of being a 'cancer patient' I have felt very uncomfortable about the philosophy and the practice offered by the medical profession in the N.H.S.

Also, with my experience of nursing in different areas over a period of more than twenty years, I appreciate that many health professionals are very caring and compassionate, yet have their hands tied as to what treatment can be offered.

As a result of the research carried out since my diagnosis I have become more aware of so many other people sharing similar feelings.

I am not attacking the medical profession, but fiercely oppose the enormous power that drug companies have over various professionals in order to make huge profits with no consideration for the 'cancer patients.'

Phillip Day supports this by writing in "Health Wars (2001) "The medical/pharmaceutical industry is unlikely to gain an overnight morality and be the first to advise us to take proper care of ourselves to help prevent heart disease and cancer. Politicians on occasion however have attempted to redress the problem. The Dietary Goals for the United States, for instance, prepared by the Select Committee on Nutrition and Human Needs, declares:

"As a nation we have come to believe that medicine and medical technology can solve our major health problems. The role of such important factors as diet in cancer and heart disease has long been obscured by the emphasis on the conquest of these diseases through the miracles of modern medicine. Treatment, not prevention, has been the order of the day.

The problems can never be solved merely by more and more healthcare. The health of individuals and the health of the population is determined by the variety of biological, behavioural and environmental factors. None of these is more important than the food we eat."

I have also had meetings with my local M.P. The aim is to make some changes in the law that will enable us to have a choice of treatment still paid for by the N.H.S. because, so far, it would appear that treatment down the pathway that I have followed works out cheaper than the original treatment offered, hence this would mean that more patients could be treated within the same budget.

We don't have to settle for strategies of containment whilst waiting for scientists to discover that magical cure for cancer. Seminars that I have attended, books which I have read and further research have given evidence of successful multimodal alternative approaches to cancer. Nobody will ever speak in terms of a 'single cure.' Multiple treatments and substances work together, synergistically, to effect major changes in the cancer process, from containment to remission to a life that is cancer free.

Cancer reversal is possible, yet requires effort, commitment and trust on the part of the person involved. A physician with comprehensive knowledge of the modalities available and their effectiveness in clinical practice will also increase the chances.

Professor Jane Plant, CBE, one of Britain's most eminent scientists, contracted breast cancer in 1987. Following five recurrences, by 1993 it had spread to her lymph system. However, by using her training and knowledge as a natural scientist, to make certain lifestyle changes she was able to over come it, and confirms that "Knowledge is Power."

"Being diagnosed with cancer has introduced me to myself and helped me find the way through."

CONCLUSION

Cancer possibly became apparent to wake me up – to change priorities in my lifestyle and my way of thinking. It has also changed lives of those around me, hopefully for the better.

One of the lessons was learning how much I am loved by others! I have stopped taking life for granted and do not want to put off until tomorrow what I can do today. Neither has it gone without notice that others around me sometimes show more awareness of the time factor. I have been a healthy eater for many years, yet am now more aware of how important it is.

Another important step was that of learning to love myself. This may have been the most difficult task, yet it is a pleasure to say that, as a result, fulfilment has been achieved and I encourage all readers to do the same.

I seem to have quickly learned ways of eliminating everyday stress and anger, which played part in my life prior to being diagnosed. Cancer has taken me beyond the point of worrying. I now view many things from a different perspective. I have also been able to adjust my lifestyle in order to keep the restored defensive network in balance.

This experience has helped confirm how important it is to be guided by one's own inner feelings. I believe that because of the holistic approach, my body's own healing powers have been brought back into balance and are now working. I also feel that more people need to be made more aware of this.

The early days following my diagnosis were very much like being on a roller coaster. I experienced shock, anger, disbelief, fear, panic, sadness, helplessness and hopelessness, which, I suppose is only to be expected. Like many others in a similar position, I managed to overcome this "adjustment disorder" with time and support from family and friends.

I appreciate how fortunate I was to have all this help at hand and now hope that others less fortunate than myself will have gained knowledge and strength from reading my story and with the help of the lists at the back of the book can find a similar pathway for themselves.

Relationships of this quality don't happen automatically, yet are achievable.

Another desire is that after reading about my experience, others will realise how vital it is to stop and think, hence allowing oneself to 'feel' an awareness of *why* we sometimes feel 'off balance.' Often in moments of great stress, we have exclaimed, "I wish I could stop the world, I want to get off!" This is exactly what natural therapies can do. They encourage us to 'stop and get off.' It may only be for a short period, yet we are able to step back and look at 'things' more clearly, becoming more aware of exactly what is going on. We are then able to get back into the world, possibly making changes to live in a more healthy and constructive manner.

Because mental, emotional and spiritual being influences one's life, I feel it is important to make the medical staff more aware of this. Many carefully monitor the physical signs and symptoms yet pay no attention to how the condition is affecting the person's life. Work, marriage, family and mental adaptation also need to be considered.

One thing that does upset me is the struggle, both mentally and financially I had to go through to receive the treatment I wanted – not what our government policy says is acceptable. I feel that no matter what the illness is the individual should be able to have some say in what type of treatment they want.

Conventional, traditional and complementary medicine would mean safer, better cost effective healthcare. More money needs to be invested into prevention of illness and maintaining good health.

We should also be made more aware of the side effects conventional treatment may cause and the decision of whether to go ahead should be left up to us. Consent forms may be signed explaining the chosen route.

I also feel that the public should be made more aware of being responsible for their own well-being. Complementary therapies need to be recognised and incorporated into the N.H.S. They could be prescribed, to a greater extent, in order to give relief from the more common ailments and chronic diseases, the effect of which often outshines conventional treatment.

Most doctors are used to passive obedience and do not want their patients to confuse the statistics. I felt that one of my consultants appeared rather narrow minded, being led by 'statistics' yet unable to provide them when requested.

Generally I found the medical team in the N.H.S. very 'one sided'. The treatment consisted of a rather narrow path i.e. surgery, chemotherapy and radiotherapy. The quality of one's life was not considered. I appreciate that this form of treatment may be suitable for others yet still feel that treatment should entail more ingredients such as diet, exercise, relaxation etc. Compared with making a cake, the main ingredients may be there and it can turn out alright yet those few extras can make such a difference to the finished product. Also, if the ingredients go out of balance, it becomes apparent in the end result.

"Cancer" has become a big business in the pharmaceutical industry and there is evidence that many more people make 'big money' from it. Pharmaceutical companies also have great influence over what doctors/nurses are taught (I attended lunches organised by these companies, whilst in my nursing career). Many people are simply prepared to accept what is said and although others may wish to do further research, time is limited, hence they find themselves on the treadmill falling into the rhythm of what is being practised around them.

Research has shown that the death rate linked to breast cancer is escalating out of control, especially in the U.K. More people need to make effort towards looking at reasons why this should be and ways of controlling it.

I was fortunate enough to meet a doctor who had done research into less invasive treatment routes for cancer and supported my own feelings of what treatment was required. My awareness of other doctors offering similar treatments has also become more apparent – we need more people like this to come forward.

I would like to stress that my G.P. was very supportive - he listened to my views and supported my choice of treatment – this illness may have built more of a rapport between us and I hope that he has been able to learn something from it as well. My thanks go out to him because, as mentioned before, relationships definitely have some affect on the prognosis.

I feel that I am one of the fortunate ones that has been able to find another suitable treatment route and have enjoyed sharing it with others by writing this book. The main purpose is to help as many people as possible to benefit from the knowledge of my experience.

I also appreciate that cancer may not be cured for some people, yet being able to live a comfortable lifestyle with pain or any other discomfort under control surely would be more acceptable.

If you are suffering with cancer already you may be able to improve your condition and get more out of life. If you are fortunate enough to enjoy good health, you can keep it that way, maybe improve and prevent ill health occurring.

Having had the opportunity to relate some of my experience to you I hope that reassurance is given to others that being diagnosed with cancer does not mean that one's life has come to an end – in many cases it is only just the beginning!

Update (since writing the book)
Early 2002

I often find it difficult to believe that I was ever diagnosed with breast cancer and need to look back at my diary and photographs.

Generally, I have taken more notice of my own intuition. I listen to my body's needs and treat it with respect.

I have learned to accept that my body requires rest and now enjoy this rather than feel guilty about 'sitting down'.

The original 'lump' appears to have gone. Receiving chemotherapy meant I had to adapt to sudden menopausal changes, which were not too pleasant, at times. However, I am still aware of a 'hormonal cycle' taking place and this appears to have some influence on how my breast feels.

There was a small scare last year when I visited my osteopath asking for assistance with pain relief in my lower back. Following examination, he said that he did not want to give treatment until I consulted my G.P. for further X-rays. I explained that a bone scan had not revealed any cause for concern, only degeneration of L4 (one of the lumbar vertebræ), yet he replied "a lot can happen in six months."

This comment obviously lowered my spirit and it must have been apparent in my facial appearance because Thomas took one look at me a few hours later and asked if anything was wrong.

I am pleased to say that the next day, following an appointment for reflexology with Pat, I came home feeling reassured and positive thinking.

Giving it further thought, I still felt that I should consult my G.P. about the matter because my osteopath had helped in the past and I still wanted to remain on his list of clientele.

On consultation with my G.P. he explained that X-rays were not very diagnostic in cases like this. He also wanted to examine me and showed some concern over what was felt. I explained that it was pointless referring me back to the oncology dept. because if any secondaries should become apparent, routine treatment would be chemotherapy, which I still had no desire to have.

As always, he supported my feelings and suggested that he contacted the rheumatoid consultant instead, with a view to seeking pain relief. I appreciated his concern and gave my approval.

Whilst awaiting this appointment, it was suggested, from another source, that I increased my intake of apricot kernels in order to improve the analgesic effect as well as targeting any more cancer cells, if they were apparent.

This was carried out and I am pleased to write that it had the desired effect. *Phillip Day states in his book Cancer Why we're still dying to know the truth* that analysis of laetrile reveals a molecule of benzaldehyde, which is a known analgesic.

By the time my appointment came round for further consultation I was able to say "because I am now able to live a comfortable lifestyle I would prefer not to have any further investigations carried out." Also believing the saying that 'very often ignorance is bliss', this was the route I wanted to follow.

Following examination by the consultant, he agreed that there was not any need for further investigations if I was comfortable.

Michael was also fortunate to have another job offered to him early last year, which was accepted.

Thomas won a scholarship for a catering course, which started in September and is doing really well. It entails living away from home and he has matured very quickly.

James started secondary school education in September and appears to have settled in well.

Change of house has also taken place.

Whilst out for a cycle ride with Michael in March 2001 he commented that we should consider purchasing a bungalow that we noticed was "For Sale" with a view to making alterations to it.

This had quite a profound influence on me. The fact that he considered taking such a large step obviously meant that he agreed 'I was cured' and this made me feel well and truly 'back to normal' again. I was elated.

Anyway, on making further enquiries, somebody else had started the procedure of purchasing this property. Obviously, I was initially disappointed, yet at the same time felt that was how it was meant to be.

Three months later, we viewed a house that we both found appealing and put an offer forward, which was accepted. We eventually moved into it at the end of October and have found it to be very inspiring – another new direction in my lifestyle.

It felt like the right time to visit our local M.P. again.

Michael and I made an appointment to see him, in November 2001, only to have it confirmed that we can't beat the system – money being saved or one's inner feelings and comfortable well being doesn't appear to have any influence on the treatment that is offered on the N.H.S. His response was "The medical establishment is very set in it's ways and is so slow moving, that it will take a long time to change it's views."

It appears that the system does not want to entertain anyone whose views are out of step with it's own.

The conclusion was that he would keep a check on the subjects for investigation by the Health Committee, in both the Commons and the Lords. When an appropriate subject comes up, he will contact me with a view to submitting evidence and the possibility of being called.

Could this enable me to make a small contribution towards some changes in the approach towards cancer treatment?

"Maybe a small spark could become a flame."

Unfortunately, a multitude of people still look upon cancer as a 'tragic illness' with the misunderstanding that it is a fatal disease. Many remain ignorant that there are numerous ways to safeguard oneself against it – prevention is still better than a cure.

One needs to remember that the medical establishment is still inclined to treat the disease (whilst making great profits for pharmaceutical companies) instead of going further forward in educating the public of natural ways to maintain good health.

I feel that this is where I would like to take part. Having already been approached to share some of my experience with local groups, I am pleased to say, that positive feedback has been received.

My aim is to continue this pathway in order to increase one's awareness of preventive measures that can be taken, along with alternative routes of treatment for cancer should it be needed. To see reversal in the tide of chronic illness and a true decrease in the diagnosis of cancer would be overwhelmingly satisfying.

Whilst writing this book, I was fully aware of the fact that modern medicine has reached a crossroads. Although it has many areas of excellence, such as emergency treatments and reconstructive surgery, it still has many areas of weakness, especially concerning chronic degenerative disorders and the psychological aspect of illness. These problems, along with a growing concern over increasing incidences of iatrogenic diseases (those caused by medical treatment) has led to not only patients, but those trained in the medical profession as well, seeking a substantial defection away from orthodox medicine.

Another reason for writing this book is to help others who feel they want to take as much responsibility as possible for their own health and well-being.

REFERENCES

Courtney H.	1995	What's The Alternative? *Infinity Press, Birmingham*
Meares A.	1978	The Wealth Within *Hill of Content Publishing Company Pty Ltd. Australia.*
Charles R.	1990	Mind, Body and Immunity. *Cedar Health U.K., London*
Issels J.	1999	Cancer A Second Opinion *Avery Publishing Group, New York*
Day P.	1999	Cancer – Why We're Still Dying to Know the Truth *Credence Publications, Tonbridge, Kent*
Day P.	2001	Health Wars *Credence Publications, Tonbridge, Kent*
Ransom S.	2001	Plague, Pestilence and the Pursuit of Power *Credence Publications, Tonbridge, Kent*
Worwood V.	1990	The Fragrant Pharmacy *Macmillan, London*
Lazarides L.	1996	Nutritional Therapy *Thorsons, London*
Lang S Patt R.	1994	You Don't Have to Suffer *Oxford University Press, New York*
Pilkington P.	2000	Centrepiece Spring 2000 Issue 34 'Pioneering Doctor' *Bristol Cancer Help Centre Newsletter*

Kidman B.	1983	A Gentle Way With Cancer *Arrow Books Ltd. London WC2N 4NW*
Briffa Dr. J.	2001	Attacking Breast Cancer Naturally *Daily Mail, Good Health Alternative* *February 27th*
Daily Mail	2002	Eat for immunity, Colour supplement *January 2002*
Regelson W. Colman C.	1996	The Super Hormone Promise *Pocket Books, New York NY 10020*
Wright C.	1998	Overcoming the sweet temptation *Healing Points ISSN 1369-1775* *The Holistic Association of* *Reflexologists.*
Magee F.	2000	Reflexology and Cancer Care *Reflexions September 2000 Issue 60*

BIBLIOGRAPHY

Walters R.	1993	OPTIONS The Alternative Cancer Therapy Book *Avery Publishing Group, New York*
McTaggart L.	1997	The CANCER Handbook. What's Really working *What Doctors Don't Tell You Publication.*
Bishop B.	1985	A Time To Heal *Penguin Books Ltd., London*
Binzel P.	1994	Alive and Well *American Media, California*
Daniel R.	1996	Healing Foods. *Thorsons, London*
Sen J.	1996	Healing Foods Cookbook. *Thorsons, London*
Kenton L.& S.	1985	Raw Energy Recipes *Century Publishing London*
Holford P.	1998	100% Health *Judith Piatkus Ltd., London*
Jochems R.	1994	Dr. Moerman's Anti Cancer Diet. *Avery Publishing Group*
Meek J.	1996	Boost Your Immune System. *ION Press, London*
Batmanghelidj F.	1992	Your Body's Many Cries For Water *The Therapist Ltd, Henry House, Heene Road, West Sussex BN11 4NN*
Mason K.	2000	Thoughts that harm, Thoughts that Heal *Judy Piatkus Ltd., London*

Meares A.	1967	Relief Without Drugs. *Souvenir Press*
Hay L.	1984	You Can Heal Your Life. *Eden Grove Editions, Middlesex*
Various Authors	1998	Vol. 28 The Ecologist *Ecosystems Ltd., Newton, Dorset*
Picardie R.	1998	Before I Say Goodbye *Penguin Books, London*
Scully J.	1995	Marion: A Modern Day Miracle *Basement Press, Dublin 2*
Vernon C. Hand J.W.	1995	Hyperthermia in the Treatment of Cancer. Treatment of Cancer, third edition *Chapman & Hall, London*
Goodman S.	1988	Germanium. The health and life Enhancer *Thorsons, Northamptonshire*
Steinman D. Epstein S.	1995	The Safe Shopper's Bible *Macmillan, Broadway, New York*
Moss R.	1995	Questioning Chemotherapy *Equinox Press, New York*
Le Shan	1984	You Can Fight For Your Life *Thorsons Northamptonshire*
Kuner Orsborn Quigley Stroup	1999	Speak the Language of Healing *Conari Press, Berkeley, California*
Gillanders A.	2001	Compendium of Healing Points *Ann Gillanders*

Finch K .	2001	Reflexology For Cancer Patients Healing Points June 2001 *Guild of Complementary Therapists,* *Berkshire RG40 4NS*
Barron P.	1996	The Natural Way Cancer *Element Books Ltd. Dorset SP7 8BP*
Lang S. Patt R.	1994	Don't Have To Suffer *Oxford University Press*
Kent A.	1996	Life After Cancer *Ward Lock, 125 Strand, London* *WC2R OBB*
Faulder C.	1995	Breast Cancer and Breast Care *Ward Lock, 125 Strand, London* *WC2R OBB*
Richards B. Hourigan F.		The Even Better Good News About Cancer *PO Box 75 Sandwich, Kent CT13 9RT*
Myss C.	1997	Anatomy of The Spirit – The Seven *Stages of Power and Healing* *Bantam Books, London*
Pert C. B.	1997	Molecules of Emotion Why you feel the Way you feel *Simon & Schuster UK Ltd* *LondonWC2B 6AH*
Rollason H.	2000	Life's Too Short *Hodder & Stoughton, London NW1 3BH*
Castle F.	2000	Cancer's a Word, not a Sentence *Hodder & Stoughton, London NW1 3BH*

USEFUL CONTACTS

Bristol Cancer Help Centre
Information: 0117 980 9500
Helpline: 0117 980 9505
E-mail: info@bristolcancerhelp.org
Website: www.bristolcancerhelp.org

BACUP 0800 18 11 99
Website: www.cancerbacup.org.uk

Cancer Alternative Information Bureau
Website: www.caib.co.uk.

Cancerlink 08088 080 000

Breast Cancer Care 0808 800 6000

The London Haven Sponsoring those affected by breast cancer
020 7384 0099

Macmillan Cancer Relief Information Line
0845 601 6161

Cancer Research Campaign
10 Cambridge Terrace
London NW1 4JL
020 7317 5027

Liongate Clinic
8 Chilston Road, Tunbridge Wells
Kent TN4 9LT   01892 543535

Centre for Alternative Medicine Research in Cancer
http://www.sph.uth.tmc.edu/utcam

National Action Plan on Breast Cancer
http://www.napbc.org

The Complementary Cancer Care Trust
01322 524079

Royal London Homeopathic Hospital
Tel. 0171 837 8833

International Society of Professional Aromatherapists
Tel. 01455 637987

Research Council for *Complemenary Medicine*
Tel. 0207 833 8897

Association of Reflexologists
0870 5673320

Dr. Edward Bach Centre
Tel. 01491 834678

National Federation of Spiritual Healers
Tel. 0891 616080

British Wheel of Yoga
Tel. 01529 306851

Newways Products
Kathryn Varley
Tel. 01245 361385

Vegan Society
Tel. 01424 427393

Vegetarian Society
Tel. 0161 925 2000

Gerson Support Group
Tel. 01372 817652

Simply Organic (Home Shopping)
Tel. 0845 1000 444
Website: www.simplyorganic.net

Taste of The Wild
High quality special dietary, Organic
and natural foods.   *Tel. 0118 954 2263*
Website: www.tasteofthewild.co.uk

Goodness Direct
More than 1,000 products for
those with special dietary needs.
Tel. 0871 871 6611

APPENDICES

Chapter 25

What Causes Cancer? Its Origin Is Multifactorial

If there is a single truth about cancer that is beyond argument, according to the clinical results and testimonies of the many physicians consulted for this book, it is that cancer has multiple, interacting causes. Many interdependent factors—at least 33—in various combinations can contribute to the development of cancer in a given individual.

I f there is a single truth about cancer that is beyond argument, according to the clinical results and testimonies of the many physicians consulted for this book, it is that cancer has multiple, interacting causes. As much as science strives to identify *single* precipitating factors—such as genes or infectious organisms—practitioners of alternative medicine know there is no single cause for cancer, just as there is no single magic bullet therapy or substance to end it. Many *interdependent* factors contribute to the development of cancer. In fact, this chapter will present detailed information on 33 distinct contributing factors that, in various combinations, can begin a cancer process in a given individual.

**A Gradual Systemic Poisoning
Then Weakening of the Body**

The concept that cancer is the result of multiple factors impinging on an individual's mind, body, and organic systems is actually not a new one, but it is one that has been consistently ignored by conventional cancer doctors. For example, in 1958, Max Gerson, M.D., an alternative cancer treatment pioneer (profiled in this book under Gerson Diet Therapy in Chapter 28: Nutrition as Cancer Medicine) explained in general terms how cancer results.

First, there is a slow buildup of toxicity throughout the body, especially the liver which is responsible for most of the body's detoxification, leading to a functional alteration of most systems including the chemical balance between sodium and potassium in the cells. Next comes a lowering of electrical potentials in the vital organs, a further accumulation of poisons, a reduction in the activity and supplies of oxygen, and the preliminary mutation of some normal cells into cancer cells, said Dr. Gerson. With this, cancer starts, "general poisoning increases, vital functions and energies decrease, and cancer increases," said Dr. Gerson. There next comes a further destruction of the metabolism (energy extraction from food) and liver functioning as the "cancer rules" and spreads.[1]

Today, we talk more in terms of immune system dysfunction and perhaps less in terms of sodium and potassium balances, but Dr. Gerson's basic insight of a progressive, systemic poisoning and weakening is still valid. In fact, it is even more valid today than in the 1950s as we are routinely subjected to far more toxins in our environment today and have become increasingly aware of their harmful effects, particularly with respect to the cancer process.

As Robert O. Becker, M.D., noted authority on the health perils and medical promise of electromagnetic energy, explains, everyone is

33 Factors That Contribute to Cancer

- Sunlight
- Chronic Electromagnetic Field Exposure
- Geopathic Stress
- Sick Building Syndrome
- Ionizing Radiation
- Nuclear Radiation
- Pesticide/Herbicide Residues
- Industrial Toxins
- Polluted Water
- Chlorinated Water
- Fluoridated Water
- Tobacco and Smoking
- Hormone Therapies
- Immune-Suppressive Drugs
- Irradiated Foods
- Food Additives
- Mercury Toxicity
- Dental Factors
- Nerve Interference Fields
- Diet and Nutritional Deficiencies
- Chronic Stress
- Toxic Emotions
- Depressed Thyroid Action
- Intestinal Toxicity and Digestive Impairment
- Parasites
- Viruses
- Blocked Detoxification Pathways
- Free Radicals
- Cellular Oxygen Deficiency
- Cellular Terrain
- Oncogenes
- Genetic Predisposition
- Miasm

545

Appendix 1
Alternative Guide to Cancer *cont'd.*

constantly exposed to substances and energies, from chemicals to X rays, that can potentially start a cancer process. "As a result, we are always developing small cancers that are recognized by our immune system and destroyed." The healthy body can normally handle individual carcinogenic influences, but when they become multiple and cumulative, the body begins to weaken, and this is the point at which harmful influences may gain the upper hand. "Any factor that increases the growth rate of these small cancers gives them an advantage over the immune system," says Dr. Becker, and cancer emerges.[2]

Dr. Becker's observation underscores a key concept involving cancer: cancer cells—an estimated 300, but more if the body has been exposed to carcinogens—are created every day in healthy human beings. What's a mere 300 out of an estimated 30 trillion cells that comprise the human body? Cancer cells, in moderation, are a legitimate part of nature. The difference between a person with cancer and a person with fleeting cancer cells is that in the latter the immune system is able to eliminate the aberrant cells from the system before they are able to do any damage to the body or start an illegitimate growth process culminating in a tumor. As naturopathic physician and educator Joseph Pizzorno, N.D., explains, "When the immune system is not working well, the result is frequent or chronic infections, chronic fatigue, and, eventually, cancer."[3]

On a microscopic level, cancer is Nature's way of removing defective genetic material, says Victor Marcial-Vega, M.D., a cancer doctor profiled in Chapter 13. Cancer reflects a change or mutation in the DNA, a cell's genetic makeup, but this process is defensive and occurs all the time. "The body is creating throughout life and every once in a while something goes amiss. At this point, the body says, 'Oh, this didn't come out that well, let's get rid of it.' The purpose of a cancer cell is to signal the body to get rid of matter in the body that did not replicate normally." The immune response is the body's way of cleaning up defective DNA.

Out of billions of DNA replications occurring in the body each day, several will become abnormal and may lead to cancer. In fact, in an average lifetime, the human body goes through an estimated 10^{16} (ten thousand trillion) cell divisions. Those who practice good diet, exercise, and other preventive lifestyle measures may reduce their cancer risk as low as 10%. Despite the astronomic number of cell divisions, the body's cellular defense system is able to hold cancer incidence down to 1 case in every 10^{17}

Appendix 1
Alternative Guide to Cancer *cont'd.*

cell divisions.[4] "This is the way Nature intended it. When cancer cells oc-cur—and everyone has abnormal cells arising in their bodies throughout the day—they are readily detected and removed by a *healthy* immune system." The immune system helps maintain and revitalize the body by elim-inating cancer or otherwise abnormal cells. Only when the immune system weakens can the cancer cells multiply and spread through the body, says Dr. Marcial-Vega.

What makes the immune system weaken is a multiplicity of stress fac-tors, collectively known as carcinogens. Technically, carcinogens refer to chemicals or radiation with cancer-causing potential, but for the purposes of general understanding, we use the term carcinogen more broadly here. Carcinogens as we define them include chemicals, electromagnetic energy, faulty diet, free radicals, genetic predisposition, toxicity, radiation, para-sites, strong emotions, and viruses—among others. There are dozens of potential influences, which we will review in this chapter. These are not so much "causes" of cancer, as facilitators: they edge the body into a condition of weakness, vul-nerability, and immune dysfunction. In this con-dition, the ordinary production of a few cancer cells can gain the upper hand in the molecular life of the individual, and a cancer process is initiated.

> "When cancer cells occur—and everyone has abnormal cells arising in their bodies throughout the day—they are readily detected and removed by a healthy immune system," says Dr. Victor Marcial-Vega.

Depending on a person's biochemical and psychological makeup, cer-tain stressors will play a more primary role. The key concept is that the cu-mulative effect of many carcinogens and immune-suppressing agents all acting together is a weakening of the immune system, thereby allowing cancer cells to proliferate. In this chapter, we'll chart the activity of car-cinogens, from ones seemingly removed from the human being (sunlight and electromagnetic energy) to influences closer to the body (pesticides and polluted water), to those that change the nature of the body (food), to ones that work inside the body (free radicals), to ones that may have pre-ceded one's birth (genetic influences).

Defining a Carcinogen—Initiators and Promoters

The term "carcinogen" is an umbrella term to denote a substance or en-

547

159

Appendix 2
...............to those with a very personal interest in cancer.
A message from George Hill (Member of the British Register of
Complementary Practitioners.)
Optimum Energy Ltd, Clinic at Les Grandes Rocques Castel, Guernsey
Tel. 01481 251883

I WOULD NOT INTERFERE

WITH ANY CREED OF YOURS

NOR WANT TO APPEAR

THAT I HAVE ALL THE CURES

THERE IS SO MUCH TO KNOW

SO MANY THINGS ARE TRUE

THE WAY MY FEET MUST GO

MAY NOT BE BEST FOR YOU

AND SO I GIVE THIS SPARK

OF WHAT IS LIGHT TO ME

TO GUIDE YOU THROUGH THE DARK

BUT NOT TO TELL YOU WHAT TO SEE

The Spirit of Anac